Scholastic Literacy Skills

Spelling

STANDARD E

a c d b

q u

h o e p

s i t r

Ages 9–10

Photocopiable skills activities

Acknowledgements

Adapted from original material entitled *Spell Well* © Gordon Winch and Gregory Blaxell published by Martin Education of Horwitz House, 55 Chandos St, St Leonards 2065, NSW, Australia.

The publishers gratefully acknowledge permission to reproduce the following copyright material:
(page 101) **Penguin Books Limited** for the use of 'The Little Ghost's Song' from *Gargling with Jelly* by Brian Patten © Brian Patten (Penguin Books Ltd).

Every effort has been made to trace copyright holders and the publishers apologise for any inadvertent omissions.

Series consultant	Norma Mudd
Editor	Roanne Davis
Assistant editor	Dulcie Booth
Series designer	Paul Cheshire
Designer	Erik Ivens
Cover illustration	Lynda Murray

Designed using Adobe Pagemaker
Published by Scholastic Ltd, Villiers House, Clarendon Avenue, Leamington Spa, Warwickshire CV32 5PR
Printed by Ebenezer Baylis & Son Ltd, Worcester

© 1997, 2002 Scholastic Ltd

1 2 3 4 5 6 7 8 9   2 3 4 5 6 7 8 9 0 1

British Library Cataloguing-in-Publication Data
A catalogue record for this book is available from the British Library.

ISBN 0-439-98332-0

Contents

Supplementary units

Introduction

Scholastic Literacy Skills: Spelling is a structured spelling scheme for primary children from Years 3–6 (P4–7) and has been designed to meet children's spelling needs for these vital years of literacy development.

Good spelling is one of the most visible indications of literacy. It serves the purpose of good communication and marks the writer as one who has achieved a certain level of proficiency in literacy. It frees writers to concentrate more fully on the writing task itself. While it is important that children are given opportunities for 'free' writing, their ability to spell will not naturally improve if teaching only happens as and when individual needs arise.

Learning to spell is a developmental process and Scholastic Literacy Skills: Spelling focuses attention on the need for systematic teaching of spelling. An ongoing programme that involves the whole class in direct teaching is the best way to help children to become independent, effective spellers and fluent, confident writers. This is where Scholastic Literacy Skills: Spelling, with its unit-by-unit, context-based approach to learning and practising spellings, can help.

What should children know by the end of Year 2/P3?

Scholastic Literacy Skills: Spelling is developmentally structured to take children through the stages of spelling knowledge from Years 3–6 (P4–7). It is assumed that by the end of Year 2 (P3) children know all the letter names and sounds (especially the five vowels, and the use of the letter y as a vowel), both aurally and in written form. They should be able to form letters correctly and spell high-frequency words which observe common letter patterns (for example, can, dog, man). They should be able to spell some high-frequency but irregular words in terms of sight–sound correspondence (for example, the, my, we). The Dolch list of high-frequency words is given on page 23 and can be used (along with the National Literacy Strategy Framework for Teaching high- and medium-frequency words lists) as a quick assessment test of your class's spelling needs.

Spelling in the National Curriculum for England and Wales

Key Stage 1
Scholastic Literacy Skills: Spelling Ages 7–8 is aimed at the early stages of Key Stage 2, but it revises the following aspects of the National Curriculum for English. By the end of Key Stage 1, children should be able to:
- write each letter of the alphabet
- use their knowledge of sound–symbol relationships and phonological patterns
- recognise and use simple spelling patterns
- write common letter strings within familiar and common words
- spell commonly occurring simple words
- spell words with common prefixes and suffixes
- check the accuracy of their spelling, using wordbanks and dictionaries
- use their knowledge of word families and other words
- identify reasons for misspellings.

Key Stage 2

The National Curriculum for English at Key Stage 2 states that children should be taught:

- the meanings, uses and spellings of common prefixes and suffixes
- the spellings of words with inflectional endings
- the relevance of word families, roots and origins of words
- the use of appropriate terminology including *vowel, consonant, homophone* and *syllable.*

It also states that children should be taught the following spelling strategies:

- to sound out phonemes
- to analyse words into syllables and other known words
- to apply knowledge of spelling conventions
- to use knowledge of common letter strings, visual patterns and analogies
- to check their spelling using wordbanks, dictionaries and spellcheckers
- to revise and build on their knowledge of words and spelling patterns.

(from *The National Curriculum: Handbook for Primary Teachers in England* © Crown copyright 1999; © Qualifications and Curriculum Authority 1999)

Scholastic Literacy Skills: Spelling covers all the spelling strategies mentioned above. It introduces and explains rules, and provides opportunities for practice and revision. Using the Look–Say–Cover–Write–Check method of learning spellings, children learn to spell words and write them in personal wordbanks. They are encouraged to re-enter misspelled words into these wordbanks correctly. *Scholastic Literacy Skills: Spelling* introduces children to using a dictionary and gives practice in using a dictionary effectively (by direct teaching and regular practice). Children are also introduced to using an etymological dictionary and to using a thesaurus.

The 5–14 National Guidelines for Scotland

The 5–14 National Guidelines make specific reference to spelling in the English Language programmes of study: 'The teaching of spelling should be part of an agreed scheme… Supporting use should be made of a published spelling scheme graduated according to pupils' progress.' Explicit reference is made to the Look–Say–Cover–Write–Check strategy as being one method of teaching children to deal with mistakes. The 5–14 National Guidelines also make specific reference to the value of each child having a personal spelling book; this, in the form of the wordbank, is an important feature of *Scholastic Literacy Skills: Spelling.*

The Northern Ireland Curriculum

In discussing spelling within the context of the Writing Programme of Study, the Northern Ireland Curriculum outlines a broad progression at Key Stage 2 that reflects that built into *Scholastic Literacy Skills: Spelling* – 'from spelling common and familiar words in a recognisable way towards spelling more complex words correctly'. More specifically, it expects that at the end of Key Stage 2 children should be able to spell from memory frequently used words, to apply a variety of strategies to spell unfamiliar words and to use dictionaries and thesauruses. All these skills are addressed through *Scholastic Literacy Skills: Spelling.*

Common questions about spelling

Many teachers are unsure about how to teach spelling. Some common concerns are:
- How do I cope with varying levels of ability?
- How do I help children to look carefully at words so that they can recall them from memory and not just copy them 'thoughtlessly'?
- How do I help those children with specific difficulties in literacy-related areas?
- How do I encourage children to use dictionaries speedily and to locate the etymology of words?

Scholastic Literacy Skills: Spelling helps to answer these questions. It covers and continuously reviews all the areas of spelling required by the UK national curricula. Furthermore, it fulfils criteria for developing a holistic approach to literacy that links spelling, reading, writing, and speaking and listening.

A variety of strategies

Scholastic Literacy Skills: Spelling's approach to the teaching of spelling combines a variety of strategies based upon relevant research on how children learn to spell. These strategies include knowledge of:

1. Sound–symbol relationships

Much has been written about the irregularities in the English spelling system in terms of spelling according to the sounds we hear. In fact, the English writing system can be regarded as at least 80 per cent regular. Novice writers who spell according to sound (for example, *I haf a bic* for *I have a bike*) are able to communicate their message adequately, even if the spellings are incorrect.

It is, therefore, essential that children first learn the relationship between the names and the sounds of the 26 letters of the alphabet and also their appearance in graphic form. Later, children need to know the 44 sounds (or phonemes) in the English language (see page 22 for a list of the phonemes).

The research of Peter Bryant and Lynette Bradley, and Usha Goswami and Bryant, indicates that even very young children are usually sensitive to the sounds they hear. Children are particularly sensitive to rime (or what teachers may refer to approximately as rhyme) and onset (the first consonant/s in a word such as the *s* in *sing* and the *dr* in **drop**).

Findings indicate that children who are helped to develop their phonological awareness and sense of rhyme at an early age are likely to learn to read and spell more easily. A knowledge of the aural aspects of the writing process is integral to the approach in *Scholastic Literacy Skills: Spelling*.

2. Blends and digraphs

Though many children can detect and identify sounds in words, problems sometimes arise when they try to write what they hear as they say a word. Words which cause difficulty are those with letters that blend or run together when they are spoken (for example, *sing, stop*) or with two letters that have only one sound (these are called digraphs, of which *ea, ai, ch, ck, sh* are examples). *Scholastic Literacy Skills: Spelling* practises and revises common blends and digraphs, and encourages children to read texts aloud, listening for certain sounds while they look at the corresponding written form. This focus on careful listening and looking is a vital strategy in improving children's awareness of the 'trickier' aspects of the English spelling system.

3. Pronunciation of words

Teachers and parents can help children to spell by articulating words clearly and correctly and, when necessary, by drawing their attention to how a particular sound is voiced. It is even more helpful to show children how a particularly tricky sound looks in writing. Often, if children want to represent a sound when they are spelling a word, but have difficulty in finding a perfect fit, they will choose a near fit by using a letter that approximates to the sound they wish to represent. For example, children who have difficulty with the *th* digraph may say (and then write) *free* for *three*, or *tay/tey* for *they*. Similarly, it is common for some children to omit the *h* from *wh* words (for example, *whisper, when, where*). Some misspellings may be caused by difficulties in discriminating some sounds (see 'Helping children with spelling difficulties', page 18). Throughout *Scholastic Literacy Skills: Spelling*, children read texts aloud to themselves and/or others. Teachers may decide to read some texts aloud to the class, to model clear, correct pronunciation; this may differ according to regional accents so that, for example, the *u* sound in *book* may be pronounced as *oo*, especially in parts of Northern England.

4. Syllabification

The strategy of dividing words into syllables is helpful in several ways. It enables children to remember how to spell longer words by finding shorter, known words or roots within the longer word (for example, *know* and *edge* in *knowledge*). It can help them not to omit parts of longer words (for example, *en vi ron ment* or *dis app ear*) by focusing on short sound units (there are far fewer syllables than there are letters in the words). This strategy also reinforces correct pronunciation of words. Syllabification is a regular feature of activities in *Scholastic Literacy Skills: Spelling*.

5. Sight–symbol relationships

As novice spellers progress from the phonetic stage of spelling, they become increasingly aware that letter sounds do not always have a constant representation in writing. For example, the *as* in the word *was* is often written by novice spellers as *woz*. Such spellers begin to rely more on visual and morphemic (or meaning-bearing) clues, and need to pay special attention to the visual aspects of words. They need to work on developing a visual memory, locating difficult parts of words by looking carefully at tricky spellings. The ability to look carefully at words needs thoughtful and explicit teaching. In normal reading, it is possible to make sense of text while paying minimal attention to the spelling of individual words. A good visual memory is best achieved (especially for tricky words, for example those with irregular sound–symbol correspondences) by using the Look–Say–Cover–Write–Check method. Writers should then use the tricky words in the course of their own writing, or the words should form part of a contextualised writing activity.

6. Roots of words

Roots are the 'meaning-bearing chunks' of words. If learner spellers can identify roots, they can make sense of the fairly regular patterns of changes of meaning and spelling that occur when prefixes or suffixes are added to roots. They can then learn to build words and, conversely, to break them up to facilitate spelling, as explained in section 4 on the previous page.

7. Prefixes and suffixes from other languages

Prefixes and suffixes, when added to the root of a word, alter the meaning of the word. Many are of Latin or Greek origin. The earlier children are introduced to prefixes and suffixes, the better, as learning about them helps children to understand the meanings of new words, and consequently to spell them.

8. Word families

Independent, self-sufficient spelling should be the aim of every learner speller. A knowledge of word families (or word patterns) helps children to spell by analogy and to make an intelligent 'guess' at a spelling. It is important that children always 'have a go' at a spelling, so long as they then remember to check their guess. Word families are useful as a memory aid – the words can be put into a sentence to be learned, for example *I ought to have brought my books – I thought I had!* or *My friend has a piece of pie.* Encourage children to make up their own mnemonic sentences for words they find difficult. They could also collect new words for word families.

9. Kinaesthetic approaches

Kinaesthetic refers to the shape of a word. Kinaesthetic strategies, which involve using 3-D letters or letter shapes for children to move around to make words, or tracing over letters, are often recommended for children who experience difficulties with reading and spelling. In fact, many learner spellers benefit from this approach. The use of something tangible (for example, plastic letters or tracing in sand) can help make a learning task less abstract and transitory. For older learners, Scrabble tiles are an 'adult' version of the same approach.

10. Generalisations about the English spelling system

Many of the so-called 'rules' of spelling have exceptions to them. But if they are taught as generalisations with exceptions, they can provide a degree of security. *Scholastic Literacy Skills: Spelling* gives, practises and revises such rules in order to reduce the learning load.

Using *Scholastic Literacy Skills: Spelling*

Scholastic Literacy Skills: Spelling recognises that spelling is an integral part of the writing process, which includes grammar and punctuation, and requires an active approach so that children use and apply spellings in their reading and writing in all learning areas. It has been shown that learning spellings in isolation is not an effective way of ensuring this integration. *Scholastic Literacy Skills: Spelling* encourages children to work at improving their spelling in different contexts, giving relevance to the spelling task. It includes lively rhymes, poems, puzzles, jokes, short stories and information texts which hold children's attention, foster discussion and close engagement with texts. This approach gives real opportunities to both extend children's knowledge and to show them that learning to spell can be fun.

The four books in the series provide continuity, progression and flexibility for all the children in a class and are not merely collections of lists of words to be tested weekly. The supplementary photocopiable sheets in each book allow teachers to differentiate tasks even more finely, tailoring the units to suit individual needs.

General approaches

Scholastic Literacy Skills: Spelling is designed to be used flexibly in the classroom. Teachers will decide which approaches best suit their children. Some general approaches are:

Whole-class approach

If each child has a copy of the same unit, the spelling needs of the children can be met through progress as a class. This allows the whole class to work simultaneously on a shared text.

Group approach

This approach enables different-ability groups to work on different units. *Scholastic Literacy Skills: Spelling* caters for sequential development so that each photocopiable book dovetails into the next. This provides opportunities for flexible planning of a spelling programme. Exercises can be related to ongoing class work and/or projects. So, for example, when adjectives and nouns are discussed, it might be helpful to look at *Spelling Ages 8–9* (pages 70–1); or if word origins are discussed, the unit on etymology in *Spelling Ages 10–11* (pages 106–7) could be used.

Skills-focus approach

Scholastic Literacy Skills: Spelling permits a systematic development of spelling skills suited to the different linguistic levels of children. In a class of eight- to nine-year-olds, for example, children of average ability in spelling (which may be most of the class) may work on units from *Spelling Ages 8–9*, while more able spellers work on units from *Spelling Ages 10–11*. Children who find spelling difficult may work on units from *Spelling Ages 7–8*, using the supplementary photocopiable pages to reinforce learning.

Teachers could spend between five and ten minutes explaining work to the 'average' spellers, while the less able spellers could be paired to test each other on spellings entered in their wordbanks. More able spellers could begin working unaided (initially). This helps children become accustomed to following instructions independently. After the first five or ten minutes, teachers will be available to give time to the less able spellers, explaining tasks carefully, checking their self-tests or revising recently learned work.

Using the units

Teachers can read instructions, poems and texts both to and with the children, especially less able spellers and readers. This is particularly recommended when using units from the books for *Spelling Ages 7–8* and *Spelling Ages 8–9*.

Make sure that children become familiar with the technical vocabulary used in the units (for example, *underline, complete, fill in, consonant, vowel (long* and *short), singular, plural* and so on). Don't forget that some children have difficulties in distinguishing left from right.

Ensure that children understand fully the Look–Say–Cover–Write–Check method of learning spellings. Encourage them to look carefully and to identify and underline tricky words or parts of words. Many novice spellers simply glance at a word to be learned without noting the shape of the individual letters. Model this strategy explicitly and often. Remind children regularly of the strategy when undertaking written work.

Effective proof-reading also requires modelling. The checking of work needs to be done quite slowly, word by word, if errors are to be detected. Making up mnemonics is something children enjoy, but remind them that their purpose is to remember how to spell a word. For example, if the sentence *The bus is busy* is used to aid the spelling of *bus*, then it should be explained that *busy* contains the word *bus*; this part of the word should be underlined.

Wordbanks

A photocopiable wordbank is provided on pages 112–18. It lists every word taught in the main units of this book, and has alphabetical headings so that children can have practice in developing skills using alphabetical order.

Setting up children's individual wordbanks is also important and children should be encouraged to use theirs as a quick reference for all written work. This should become a matter of instinct for children, but in the early stages regular use needs to be encouraged. Some children may be reluctant to re-enter words they misspell. It is, however, vital that they do re-enter words (particularly high-frequency words) that cause them difficulty. Each child and teacher will then be able to flick through the wordbank and quickly identify tricky words. For example, if *because* is entered three or four times, this indicates that the word needs specific attention.

Targeting tricky words

In the course of working on the activities, children are asked to make up their own sentences using target words. Encourage children to use words they have learned but found tricky. This means they will constantly revise high-frequency words that they find difficult. For example, if two of the words appearing several times in a child's wordbank are *because* and *should*, and an exercise asks for original sentences using words ending in *tion*, the child may write: *He **should** go to the sta**tion because** his friend is coming by train.*

Review units

The review units, which occur after every six units in the main section of the book, provide records of individual progress and highlight difficulties. Pairs of children can use the pages to test each other. Discuss progress with individual children, noting any difficulties that need specific attention.

Make sure children understand each part of the Look–Say–Cover–Write–Check method of learning spellings. It is important that they look carefully at the words to improve their visual memory. Saying the words helps them to associate the sounds with the visual appearance of the letters. Writing the words helps them to 'feel' the shape of the letters through the hand, especially if joined-up handwriting is encouraged from an early age. They must understand how and why to check their written work, using their wordbank or a dictionary to confirm that either their spellings are correct or that further practice may be needed.

Involving parents

Parents can give vital help, support and encouragement to their children as they progress towards becoming effective spellers. If parents are to support their children positively so that spellings are regarded as part of the wider writing process and not simply a list of unconnected words, they need to be made aware of the school's approach to teaching and improving spelling. Invite parents who are willing to help their children with their written work into school and talk through the school's philosophy and strategies for teaching writing and spelling.

Encourage parents to:
● take an interest in their child's writing at home. They should read it and give relevant praise for effort and content. They should avoid commenting firstly (or worse still only) on spelling errors, presentation and handwriting.
● involve their child in 'real' writing tasks, such as shopping lists, invitations, letters and notes to friends and relatives, diary entries and similar activities.
● help their child to 'edit' their written work and encourage the use of wordbanks and/or dictionaries to check spellings.
● have spelling games for fun – in the car, around the table, at bedtime.
● use the Look–Say–Cover–Write–Check approach to learning to spell words. Parents may need careful, explicit demonstrations of this method if they did not encounter it in their school days.
● hear their child spell for fun.
● help their child to be aware of spellings around them, for example instructions on videos or washing machines; road signs; food labels. This awareness does not mean that the child has to learn the spellings, but it helps to impress the importance of written communication as part of everyday life.

Above all, stress to parents that learning sessions should be brief and fun, and should always include plenty of praise for effort and progress. Involving parents in this way helps to develop a positive attitude in the child, which is such an important part of becoming an effective and independent speller.

How to correct spellings

Encouraging children to identify problem words and tricky parts of words for themselves begins the process of developing a 'spelling conscience', which is an important part of being an effective speller. At all times, encourage children to look up and check words they are unsure of, or words which do not 'look right'. There will be occasions when you need to correct children's spelling in the course of written work. Some useful tips for correcting children's work sensitively are:
● Concentrate on correcting misspellings of words that the child ought to know how to spell at this stage (as class teacher you are in the best position to judge what these are). This not only guarantees the best use of (your) marking time but is also less demotivating for the child.
● Don't let misspellings get in the way of praise for overall writing content.
● Try to distinguish between misspelled words that should be familiar to the child, and those which are guesses at spelling new words. Judge the latter as guesses and praise good attempts – for example, the number of 'correct' letters or a good

approximation to the sound of the word or evident use of analogy (even if it is wrong).
- Whenever possible, write the whole word correctly for the child in the margin. Do not correct parts of words in the child's writing – this only confuses the writer.

Testing and assessment

Persistent misspellings are often a problem and it is important to give specific attention to children who are not progressing. Individual error analysis, not unlike the miscue analysis developed for reading, enables teachers to look more closely at the types of errors a child is making. Repeated misspellings of particular consonants, problems with spelling prefixes or vowel digraphs can be given special attention. Although time-consuming, such analysis gives important and useful information about particular areas of spelling weakness, which can then be targeted.

A simple grid can be developed to do this:

Individual error analysis sheet

Correct word	Attempted spelling	Type of error					
		initial consonant	final consonant	consonant blend	vowel	digraph	omission
cat	kat	X					
bed	bet		X				
stop	slop			X			
run	ran				X		
feet	fet					X	
ship	sip					X	

A photocopiable version of this grid can be found on page 27.

Screening tests

When Sybil Hannovy worked at the Cambridge Institute of Education, she constructed some tests that could be given to up to 20 children at a time by one teacher with another teacher in attendance. The tests take 45–60 minutes to administer. Though designed for children younger than seven years old, the writing parts of Hannovy's tests can be adapted for use with older children who are experiencing spelling difficulties.

We expect seven-year-olds to be able to hear and discriminate all the letter sounds and names as well as to be able to write them, but this is not always the case. Older children may also have difficulty with sound–symbol relationships, and knowledge of sound–symbol correspondence is a vital element in learning both to read and spell.

The following four tests are adaptations of some of Hannovy's tests that apply to the written aspects of literacy. Extend or amend the tests further to suit the needs of particular children in your class. The first three tests highlight the child's ability to connect phonemes with letters (the auditory aspects of spelling).

In the early stages of literacy acquisition, it is essential that children are able to make connections between what they hear and what they write. Once they can hear sounds correctly and can transfer what they hear into written forms, then they are ready to progress to the visual and memory stage. Research indicates that the number of letters children can identify before they start school is the strongest predictor of subsequent reading ability.

There should be no writing or alphabets visible while the children are taking the tests. You may wish to put folded screens of card between the children to prevent copying. However, this is unnecessary if only a few children are being tested.

1. Letter sounds

Say a word to the children, and repeat the initial sound. The children write the initial letter. Walk round to observe how each child is holding their pen or pencil; look at their writing posture and letter formation. Children who cannot write the answer may leave a space. Make sure that all the letters of the alphabet are tested, but not in alphabetical order. The letters *x, q* and *y* could be merely said aloud, using their letter names. Include words with common initial digraphs and blends, repeating the initial digraph or blend (for example, *ship, this, chip, Philip, clock, quick, slid, bright*). The complexity of vocabulary digraphs or blends you choose will depend on the written work of your class.

Using the results

This test highlights those letters with which children are having difficulty. Many letter sounds are similar in the way they are made. For example, the letter sounds *b, g* and *d* sound similar. In linguistics, these sounds are called stops since they 'stop' the air. Other sounds that are similar are the fricatives (made by the friction or restriction of breath in a narrow opening) such as *s, z, v, f* and *th* (as in *then* and *thin*, which some children hear and pronounce as *ven* or *fin*). The short vowel sounds (as in *pat, pet, pit, pot, put*) are also formed in similar ways (the tongue is held in slightly different positions as voiced air passes through the mouth) and can cause problems for novice writers of any age. Children who have taken the test and confused letters or left spaces may:
- be unable to differentiate aurally between certain letters, or
- lack knowledge of the correspondence between sounds and the formation of their written representation.

Having identified children's specific difficulties, you are in a position to target teaching on problem letters. Help children to identify their problem letters singly and within words aurally, before transferring them to their written form. Once single-letter difficulties have been remedied, move on to blends and digraphs that are difficult for the children. Demonstrate how 'difficult' sounds, blends and digraphs are made by exaggerating their oral formation.

2. Written vocabulary

Ask the children to write all the words they can remember in five (or more) minutes. It is essential that, at the end of the test, they read all their words aloud to the teacher to check their ability to read aloud their own writing. Some children might write *came*, for example, but then say *come*.

Using the results

This test indicates the general extent of words that the child can recall and write 'easily'. Use these 'known' words to construct further dictation exercises to improve and remedy spelling difficulties. Since these words will generally be those that the child can write confidently, they should make a good balance between new and past successful learning.

The test also reveals whether a child confuses formation of certain letters. For example, having written *wat* or *bog*, the child may say *wet* and *dog* when reading the words aloud after the test. The first error indicates confusion about the pronunciation of short vowel sounds. The second error indicates the confusion of *b* and *d*, which is a common characteristic of novice readers and writers.

To remedy the first error, spend time with the child, identifying confused vowel sounds both in isolation and within words. To tackle the second, ensure that the child is in fact able to differentiate between the sounds in spoken words. Then suggest that the child says *bat and ball* to him- or herself when forming the letter *b* (as the downstroke is formed, the child says *bat*, and as the circular movement is made, the child says *ball*). Similarly, when the child hears the *d* sound in a word, he or she should say *drum and stick* to him- or herself (as the circular part is formed, he or she says *drum* and he or she says *stick* as the downstroke is formed).

3. Three phonemes

Dictate approximately 20 three-letter words to the children for them to write down (Hannovy suggested ten words for Year 1 children). The words should include as many different consonants as possible and all the vowels (for example, *rap, beg, cot, dim, fun, hop, jig, keg, lap, sat, van, win, fox, yes, zip*). The four-letter words *quit* and *very* could be included to check the *q* sound and *y* as a vowel sound. Words containing letters and sounds that seem to be causing difficulties for particular children should also be included.

Using the results

This test reveals the child's ability to hear and differentiate consonants at the beginning and end of words, and vowel sounds within words. It reveals the child's ability to spell phonically regular words – that is, their ability to blend phonemes as well as to identify them within a given word. This test can reveal whether children can hear first and last letters clearly but not the middle vowel. For example, they might write *pn* for *pin*. Use the results of the test to work with children on specific difficulties, using letters both in isolation and in three- or four-letter words spoken and written by the child. Subsequently, incorporate the words into brief sentences for the child to write and say regularly until he or she can write them fluently. Such sentences will be very obviously contrived, but in the early stages of remediation, a child's success in the learning task is of paramount importance. Success leads to increased self-confidence and motivates the child to learn more. Keep such targeted teaching sessions brief, regular and explicit, and praise effort as well as success.

4. Sentence dictation

Dictate between four and six sentences, reading each one several times, slowly. The sentences should contain words that are familiar to the children, both aurally and visually. They should include regular and irregular spellings in terms of sound–letter correspondence. The Dolch list of high-frequency words (see page 23) is a good source of such words, as are the high- and medium-frequency lists in the National Literacy Strategy *Framework for Teaching*.

> **Using the results**
> This test gives information on the general spelling strategies used by the child. These examples are taken from three children's answers to a dictation test. The dictation sentences were:
> *He went in the house and saw a man.*
> *The man was doing some magic tricks.*

> **Child A** wrote:
> *He went in the huose and saw a man.*
> *The man was doing some magick tricks.*

Child A shows only two errors. The first error, *huose*, contains all the correct letters, indicating visual recall of the word, but with confused recall of the *ou* sequence. The second error, *magick*, may be influenced by the spelling of the next word, *trick*. Once the child has identified and underlined the errors, look at other words in the *ou* family (for example, **ou**t, **ou**r, **lou**d, m**ou**se), and discuss the use of *c* and *ck* as word endings. Construct a sentence for the child to learn and be tested on over the following few days (for example, *I went **ou**t of **ou**r h**ou**se with the magi**c** man*). If reversals of *ou* persist, compose a mnemonic for the *ou* sequence (for example, **O**h **you** are in my h**ou**se).

> **Child B** wrote:
> *He wet in the hows and saw a man.*
> *The man woss dowing sum majik trix.*

Child B shows that most (if not all) letter sounds are known, as many of the words are written according to their sound. Child B is still at what may be termed the 'invented' spelling stage. This child has minimal knowledge of high-frequency words with irregular sound–letter correspondence (for example, *he, saw, the*).

Show Child B explicitly how to look at problem words carefully and to identify the tricky parts for him- or herself. Use the child's errors to do this. For example, when looking at the word *doing* (which the child spelled *dowing*), praise him or her for having nearly all the correct letters, before asking him or her to spot the incorrect letter. Ask the child to use Look–Say–Cover–Write–Check to learn the words *do, doing, go, going*. To remedy *woss* for *was*, encourage the child to locate the word *as* within *was*.

Construct a sentence for the child to learn and be tested on over the following few days (for example, *He **was** not **do**ing his jobs, he was **go**ing in the hut*). Note that the 'new' words in the sentence are phonically regular and so should not cause difficulties for the child.

Adjust the learning load to suit different children's levels of difficulty and attention span.

> **Child C** wrote:
> *He we in the os a se a ma.*
> *The ma wos dwig mha tx.*

Child C's attempts at written communication have broken down completely. This child knows how to spell *he, in* and *the*, but leaves many words unfinished. Initial letters of words are generally correct; *os* for *house* indicates that the *h* has not been heard, or that the child is hearing the *o* and *s* sound more dominantly. This child's spelling strategies are characteristic of someone at the very earliest stage of learning to write and who has learned a few high-frequency words by heart. Identifying separate letters in words and blending letters will help this child.

Helping children with spelling difficulties

Regular reading and writing activities will help most children to become confident and efficient spellers. However, some children will find that learning to spell presents difficulties, and there are specific but varying causes for this. One cause is dyslexia whereby something goes wrong with a person's perception of words and letters. This often affects the ability to read and write. However, if teaching is tailored to individual needs, specific difficulties may be overcome. It is important, therefore, to try to find out the individual causes of these difficulties before attempts are made to remedy them.

Remediation may include teaching/revising one or more of the following:
- sound–symbol correspondence of the alphabet, including names of letters
- common and regular letter strings which may include the use of plastic letters
- awareness of irregular but high-frequency words in which the visual aspects of the words are studied
- clear articulation of words to be studied and clear articulation of the letters of the words (in sequence)
- multi-sensory approaches to the Look–Say–Cover–Write–Check method
- use of computers, word-processors, coloured pens and so on to aid motivation in learning
- use of mnemonics to aid learning
- regular use of wordbanks once spelling is improving
- very brief, but regular, informal tests on one or two sentences which contain the words learned – the aim is to ensure the child's success.

Using plastic letters to improve literacy
A useful tool for helping children with spelling difficulties is the use of plastic letters in instruction. Some research shows that less able readers (and spellers) may be unsuccessful in the aural medium since it seems too abstract. Working with the concrete and tangible, such as plastic letters, can help these children. When word building with plastic letters, keep the focus letters static while moving other letters

around them. (For example, the blend *an* is kept static while *c, m, p, h* and *d, s* and *d* are placed in front and behind to make the words *an, can, man, pan, hand, sand*). Increase the complexity and difficulty of letter strings as the child progresses.

Look–Say–Cover–Write–Check

Expand the method into the following multi-sensory approach for children with difficulties. Children should:

1. **Look** carefully at the word.
2. **Say** the word and then its letters (names) in sequence.
3. **Cover** the word up.
4. **'Write'** the word, saying the whole word first, then the letter names:
   - in the air with eyes closed, or
   - on an (imaginary) desk, or
   - in wet sand.
   If all appears to be correct, then say the word and its letters to the teacher. Write the word on paper or in a wordbank (saying the word and letter names while doing so).
5. **Check** the word. If it is correct, write a tick over each correct letter, adding an extra tick if all the letters are in the correct order*.

*This way, the child feels more involved in his or her learning and progress than if the teacher takes the child's work and applies ticks (or crosses). For example, *house* would receive six ticks (one for each correct letter, and one for the correct sequence); *huose* would receive five ticks; and *hows* four ticks (one for each correct letter and one because they are in the correct order).

These procedures may seem time-consuming, but they usually apply only to a few children with severe spelling difficulties.

Motivating children with spelling difficulties

Using ICT can help to motivate children who find spelling difficult, particularly older children who are more likely to be negative in their attitude towards remedial teaching than younger ones. Word-processing, for example, can be helpful in giving higher status to the writing process – the work produced is clear and professional, and inputting words on-screen reinforces understanding of the left-to-right sequence of writing. Increasingly, even very young children are able to find their way round technological equipment, sometimes more easily than adults.

Encourage children to use computer spellcheckers. They will not impede the process of learning to spell and can be a useful aid, if children know about the pitfalls of using them. Make sure they understand that spellcheckers do not eliminate errors entirely as they cannot recognise grammatical relationships in sentences. It is important that children know when to 'overrule' the spellchecker.

Once confidence in spelling has been restored, and progress made and maintained, children should balance traditional methods of writing with using the computer. The use of coloured pens, pencils and paper can also stimulate children's motivation.

Bibliography

Bryant, PE & Bradley, L (1985) *Rhyme and Reason in Reading and Spelling*, University of Michigan Press.

DfEE/QCA (1999) *The National Curriculum: Handbook for Primary Teachers in England.*

Department of Education Northern Ireland (1996) *The Northern Ireland Curriculum Key Stages 1 and 2.*

Ehri, LC (1991) 'Learning to read and spell words' in L Rieben and C Perfetti (eds) *Learning to Read: Basic Research and its Implications*, Lawrence Erlbaum Associates.

Goswami, U & Bryant, PE (1990) *Phonological Skills and Learning to Read*, Lawrence Erlbaum Associates.

Hannovy, S (1991) 'Middle infant screening test: a safety net for teachers' in *Reading*, 25, no. 3, 10–15, Blackwell for UKRA.

Morris, JM (1984) 'Phonics 44 for initial literacy in English' in *Reading*, 18, no. 1, Blackwell for UKRA.

Mudd, NR (1994) *Effective Spelling: A practical guide for teachers*, Hodder & Stoughton in association with UKRA.

Peters, ML (1985) *Spelling: Caught or Taught?* (A New Look), Routledge.

The Scottish Office Education Department (1991) *National Guidelines English Language 5–14.*

Temple, C, Nathan, R, Burris, N & Temple, F (1993 3rd edition) *The Beginnings of Writing*, Allyn and Bacon Inc.

Todd, J (1982) *Learning to Spell: A Book of Resources for Teachers*, Simon & Schuster.

Teaching content and skills grid

- Introduces children to words of a more 'sophisticated' nature (for example, *tragic* and *collision*) so that they develop vocabulary knowledge as well as spelling ability.
- High-frequency (but often tricky) words are revised constantly (for example, *where/ were, thought* and *because*).
- Continued use of the Look–Say–Cover–Write–Check strategy of learning spellings.
- Introduction of dictionary page layout. Strategies for locating words are explored and consideration given to words with multiple meanings.
- Introduction of etymological dictionaries and their use in exploring word origins (for example, *spaghetti* and *kayak*).
- Children are encouraged to check word meanings as well as spellings so that homophones are not confused.
- Increased use of Latin and Greek prefixes to improve spelling and understanding of word meanings.

The grid on the facing page matches teaching content to pages.

Skill	Page numbers
Blends, digraphs and single letters	
long a	84, 129, 149
ar	48
au	46, 120
augh	85, 150
aw	30–1, 120
c/ck	61, 104, 138, 160
ea	84, 126, 149
ei/ie	28–9, 119
eigh	84, 149
ey	84, 149
ir/ur	48, 131
gh	62, 139
le	36, 91
nd	60, 137
nt	60, 137
o	70–1, 141
oa	42–3, 126, 136
oe	70–1
old	141
oll	141
oo	98, 100, 156
oor	58, 136
or	58, 136
ore	58, 136
ough	85, 150
ow	56–7, 135
scr	73, 143
sh	32, 121
sion	87, 151
sl	32, 121
sm	32
sp	32, 121
spr	73, 143
st	32, 60, 121, 137
str	73, 143
tion	43, 59
ture	60
ui	81
y	99, 157
Soft letters (c, g)	50, 53, 132

Skill	Page numbers
Spelling rules	
Doubling letters after CVC	36
Adding ing, d and ed	36–7, 124
ei or ie spellings	28–9, 50, 132
Magic e	80, 147
Homophones and near homophones	35, 38–9, 90, 102–3, 105, 125, 153
Plurals – s, es, ies, ves	37, 43, 72, 75, 122, 142, 144
Irregular plurals	33
Prefixes, suffixes and roots	51, 64–5, 74, 86, 88–9, 133, 140, 151–2
Latin and Greek words	64–5, 86, 88–9, 92, 140, 151–2
Acronyms	106–7
Punctuation and grammar	
Abbreviation	76–7, 145
Apostrophe of omission	34–5, 63, 86–7
Compound words and portmanteaux	52, 75, 134, 154
Contractions using is, not and will	34–5, 63, 86–7, 105, 123
Exclamation marks	61, 101
Full stops	76
Semicolons	86
Irregular verbs	52
Verb tenses	52
Dictionary skills and alphabetical order	44–5, 47, 66–7, 78–9, 92–5, 108–9, 127, 128, 146, 155
Silent letters	
l	49
h	101, 159

List of the 44 phonemes in English

20 vowel sounds

Short vowel sounds

apple
egg
ink
orange
umbrella
p**o**tato (this has an indistinct vowel sound or *schwa*)

Long vowel sounds

ape	p**ai**n	s**ay**
eve	p**ee**l	s**ea**l
ice	l**ie**	h**igh**
m**o**de	s**oa**k	t**oe**
fl**u**te	p**oo**l	

Other vowel sounds

b**a**ll	w**a**lk	s**aw**
st**ar**		
b**ir**d	h**er**mit	
h**oo**k		
m**ou**th	cl**ow**n	
c**oi**l	b**oy**	
sq**uare**	ch**air**	
ear	d**eer**	h**ere**
g**ou**rd	p**oor**	

24 consonant sounds

bat
cat (**k**it)
din
fish
go
have
jump
let
man
net
pat
run
set
tap
violin
want
yet
zoo (hou**s**es)
shop
chin
the
thing
si**ng**
televi**si**on

Some other consonant patterns

double consonants: *ff, ck*
clusters (initial): *sk, sp, st, cl, cr, scr, str*
clusters (end): *sk, sp, st, ps, nds, nks*
silent letters: *knit, thumb*

NB *q* and *x* are redundant as 'basic' phonemes.

Dolch list

These 100 words make up, on average, one half of all reading.

The 100 next most used words.

a	and	he
I	in	is
it	of	that
the	to	was
all	as	at
be	but	are
for	had	have
his	him	not
on	one	said
so	they	we
with	you	about
an	back	been
before	big	by
call	came	can
come	could	did
do	down	first
from	get	go
has	her	here
if	into	just
like	little	look
made	make	more
me	much	must
my	no	new
now	off	old
only	or	our
other	out	over
right	see	she
some	their	them
then	there	this
two	up	want
well	went	were
what	when	where
which	will	who
your		

after	again	always
am	another	any
away	ask	bad
because	best	bird
black	blue	boy
bring	day	dog
don't	eat	every
far	fast	father
fell	find	five
fly	four	found
gave	girl	give
going	good	got
green	hand	have
head	help	home
house	how	jump
keep	know	last
left	let	live
long	man	many
may	men	mother
Mr	never	next
once	open	own
play	put	ran
read	red	room
round	run	sat
saw	say	school
should	sing	sit
soon	stop	take
tell	than	these
thing	think	three
time	too	tree
under	us	very
walk	white	why
wish	work	would
year		

◣SCHOLASTIC

Am I a good speller?

	often	sometimes	never
I know that correct spelling is important.			
I always stop to check a spelling if I am unsure			
• by checking in my wordbank			
• by checking in a dictionary.			
I always proof-read by looking for spelling mistakes.			
I take care with my handwriting.			
I notice letter patterns like **th** and **ough**.			
I notice suffixes like **-less**.			
I notice prefixes like **dis-**.			
I learn new spellings using Look–Say–Cover–Write–Check.			
I make up mnemonics to help me remember spellings.			
My tricky words are			

Photocopiable ■ SCHOLASTIC

Indicators for novice spellers

Spelling confidence:	often	sometimes	never
spells known words automatically			
interested in new words			
tackles spellings of new words with intelligent guesses			
Spelling conscience:			
proof-reads own writing			
checks words unsure of			
● using the wordbank			
● using a dictionary			
Spelling skills:			
aware of visual patterns			
recognises many common words			
is able to spell many common words			
uses words with irregular spellings			
attempts to spell new words by analogy			
uses syllabification to learn longer words			
uses mnemonics			
understands compound words			
uses common prefixes and suffixes			
recognises roots of words			
aware that there are different ways of spelling a sound			

■ SCHOLASTIC

Name   Date

_____

Record of progress

Units		Date completed
1	Eeoww! Yieeee!	
2	Ferry ride	
3	A beachy ride	
4	Great party	
5	Crawling and wriggling	
6	Sounds the same	
7	Christmas list	
8	A to Z	
9	Special festivals	
10	Keep your shirt on	
11	Cinderella the celebrity	
12	I see, I saw	
13	A wedding day	
14	Auntie Jane's engagement	
15	Wedding celebrations	
16	The wonderful person of Sparta	
17	Unique unicorn	
18	Wonderwords	
19	Going for gold	
20	Rhinos and hippos	
21	Sports training	
22	Shorten it	
23	Seeing the carnival	
24	Record breaker	
25	Animal park	
26	Excellent skiers	
27	The maritime museum	
28	Rock pool excursion	
29	Where do words come from?	
30	Multiple meanings	
31	Show time	
32	All the fun of the fair	
33	Hear here	
34	Olympic history	
35	Scuba diving	
36	Spellcheck	

Individual error analysis sheet

Correct word	Attempted spelling	Type of error					
		initial consonant	final consonant	consonant blend	vowel	digraph	omission

Name

Objective: Spell words with the *ee* sound made by *ie* and *ei*.

Unit **1**

Eeoww! Yieee!

 When the sound made by the letters **ie** and **ei** is the same as **ee**, as in **chief**, the **i** often (but not always) comes before **e**, except after **c**.

1. Write these words in your wordbank.

| field | brief | deceive | ceiling | receive |

2. Read this story.

On my birthday, we went to the fun park. There was a man dressed up as a Native American chief.
"Good grief!" I yelled.
You would not believe how scared I was.
I let out a shriek and ran for my life.
My little sister was scared too.
When she started to cry, I gave her my handkerchief.
Afterwards, we had a piece of birthday cake.

3. Underline the **ie** words in the story that sound like **ee**.

4. Write the **ie** words that sound like **ee** in your wordbank.

5. Finish these **ie** words. Remember to Look–Say–Cover–Write–Check! (Check the meaning of **fiend**.)

br_____f   n_____ce

bel_____ve   th_____f

ch_____f   fr_____ze

f_____nd   pr_____st

 Friend is an **ie** word, but the **ie** sounds like the short **e** vowel in **met**.

6. Read these sentences aloud.

> I received a letter from my friend on my birthday.
>
> Look at the floor and look at the ceiling. Now tell me how your neck is feeling.
>
> Did you get a receipt when you paid?

7. Underline the words that follow the **ei** after **c** rule.

8. Remember that **i** does not *always* come before **e**. Write these exceptions in your wordbank.

> height   weight   eight   reign   rein
>
> vein   neighbour   Keith   Sheila

9. Read these sentences aloud, and fill in the missing letters.

The h_____ght and w_____ght of each of my fr_____nds was written on the paper.

Our n_____ghbour has _____ght chickens.

The queen r_____gned for many years.

We have v_____ns and arteries in our bodies.

If you want the horse to stop, pull on the r_____ns.

10. Watch out for these **ei** words. They also do not follow the rule! Look at them carefully, say each word, cover it, then write it in your wordbank. Remember to check each one. (Check the meaning of **weir**.)

> either   neither   seize   weir

11. Fill in the missing letters in these sentences.

S_____ze the rope and swing on it.

_____ther one will do very well.

Let's go sailing on the w_____r.

Ferry ride

 ar spells the **aw** sound in words like **warm**.

1. Read this poem aloud.

Birthday ferry ride

Come with us on the old ferry.
Be on the wharf at quarter to.
It's cold, so wear a thick, warm coat.
And bring a hat and gloves with you.

Gordon Winch

2. What words with **aw** sounds can you find in the poem? Write them in your wordbank. Find out the meaning of **wharf** and write its meaning next to the word in your wordbank.

3. Find the **aw** words in these sentences. Write them in your wordbank.

CS Lewis wrote *The Lion, The Witch and the Wardrobe*. It has been on television too.
Did you see *Snow White and the Seven Dwarfs* on your birthday?
Warning! Watch out for the swarm of bees! Oh, they're coming towards us!

4. Say these **ar** words aloud.

rew_____d   w_____d   w_____t

qu_____ter   aw_____d   wh_____f

5. In your workbook, write six sentences of your own, using words with the **aw** sound from this page.

Continued from P30   Unit **2**

 Some words spell the **aw** sound with **aw**.

6. Underline the **aw** words in these sentences, then write them in your wordbank.

We crawled across the lawn.
I saw the hawk in the sky at dawn.
It was an awful brawl.

(Check the meaning of **brawl** if you are not sure.)

The prawn trailer was at the wharf.
The wood was sawn into lengths.

7. Make **aw** words with these word parts. Say the words aloud, then write them out.

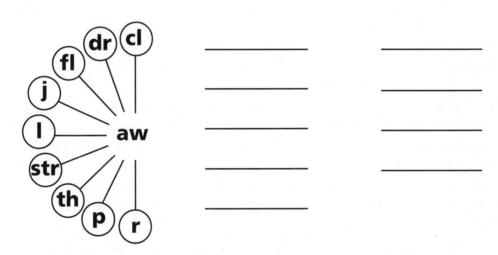

_____   _____

_____   _____

_____   _____

_____   _____

_____

8. Read these sentences aloud, and fill in the **aw** words.

Don't scr_____l on the paper. It makes an _____ful mess.

The pr_____ns are in the fridge dr_____er.

At Jim's birthday party, we drank orangeade

through str_____s.

The small puppy had four huge p_____s.

Objective: Spell words containing *s* consonant blends and digraphs.

A beachy ride

When consonants are written next to each other they are called either **consonant blends** or **digraphs**.

In a consonant blend, you can hear the separate sounds made by each consonant, like **sp ade**. You can hear **s** and **p**.

You hear a new sound with a digraph, like **sh ip**. You can hear **sh**, not **s** and **h**. The two letters have made one sound.

1. Read this story aloud. Listen to the sounds made by the consonant blends and digraphs.

Beach birthday

We went swimming at Shell Beach on my birthday. It is a small beach with many lovely shells.

The day was fine. The sky was blue and the sea sparkled. You could see ships far away from the shore. They looked small out at sea and seemed to move slowly.

When we arrived, Dad said, "Swim between the flags and stay away from the sharp rocks."

We slid down the sandhills, dug on the beach with our spades and ate slices of watermelon in the shade of the beach umbrella. We stayed all day. I wish it was still my birthday!

2. Underline all the **s** consonant blends and digraphs in the story.

Photocopiable ▲ SCHOLASTIC Continued on P33

3. Read these sentences aloud.

> I caught a fish off the wharf.
> There are hundreds of fish swimming under there.
> My cousin Jillian has a pet sheep.
> Sheep are often rounded-up by sheep-dogs.
> Mum bought a salmon at the market.
> Salmon are farmed in Scotland.

 Fish, **sheep** and **salmon** are both singular and plural forms.

4. In the sentences above, circle the words when they are singular and underline them when they are plural.

 Deer and **aircraft** are also words which are the same in singular and plural forms.

5. In your workbook, write one sentence using **deer** as singular and one sentence using **aircraft** as plural.

6. Some nouns have no singular form. Read these words aloud.

> scissors   trousers   mathematics   news   measles   gallows

(Check what **gallows** means if you are not sure.)

7. Use the words to complete these sentences.

His new _____ are too big in the waist.

There are often _____ in Western movies.

No news is good _____.

Leslie is very sick with _____.

The _____ were on the table when I last saw them.

_____ is my best subject.

Great party

If something contracts, it gets shorter. Contractions are short forms.

For example: **He is** my brother.   **He's** my brother.

He's is a contraction. **He's** is the shorter form of **He is**.

The **i** is left out with **is** contractions.

The apostrophe shows that **i** has been left out.

1. Write the full forms of these contractions. The first one has been done for you.

he's   _he is_

she's   _____

it's   _____

that's   _____

what's   _____

2. Write the contractions for these groups of words.

here is _____

John is _____

Mary is _____

3. Read this story. Then rewrite it in your workbook, writing the contractions *in full*.

He's coming to my birthday party. She's coming too. There's going to be a big cake, that's for sure! John is bringing his football. It's going to be a great party!

Continued from P34

Unit 4

It's is the shortened form of two words – **it is**.

For example: **It is** upstairs.   **It's** upstairs.

Its (without an apostrophe) refers to something belonging to **it**.

For example: **its** leg – the leg belonging to it

4. Use **its** or **it's** to complete these sentences.

I saw the man put the dog on i＿＿＿＿＿ lead.

He gave me the box and i＿＿＿＿＿ wrapping paper.

They looked at his cake and watched him blow out i＿＿＿＿＿ candles.

The horse twitched i＿＿＿＿＿ ears.

He shouted, "I＿＿＿＿＿ no use crying, we're lost."

Remember that **of** sounds like **ov**.

Off usually means there is movement.

For example: The cat ran **off**.

5. Read these sentences aloud, using **of** or **off**. Then write the correct word in each gap.

He took the present out ＿＿＿＿＿ the box.

He jumped ＿＿＿＿＿ the bus and hurt his leg.

Which ＿＿＿＿＿ you did this?

Ask her to take ＿＿＿＿＿ that big hat.

The teacher told him ＿＿＿＿＿ for being late.

Name

Objective: Add the suffixes *ing* or *ed* to verbs with *l* endings.

Unit 5

Crawling and wriggling

Verbs that end with a single **l**, but do not end with consonant–vowel–consonant (CVC), we just add **ing** or **ed**.

For example: **crawl** – **crawling** – **crawled**

1. In your workbook, add **ing** and **ed** to each of these verbs.

crawl	haul	fill	pull	kill
bawl	mail	nail	sail	

For **l** verbs that do end with CVC, we double the **l** and add **ing** or **ed**.

For example: **cancel** – **cancelling** – **cancelled**

2. Finish these word families with **ing** and **ed**.

tunnel   shovel   signal   total   swivel

For verbs that end in **le**, we drop the **e** before adding **ing**.

For example: **twinkle** – **twinkling**

Instead of **ed**, we just add **d**.

For example: **twinkled**

SCHOLASTIC Continued on P37

Name

Objectives: Add the suffixes *ing* or *ed* to verbs with *l* endings. Make plurals.

Continued from P36

Unit **5**

3. In your workbook, finish these word families with **ing** and **d**.

> buckle   jingle   sprinkle   tangle   hobble   double

4. Finish these verb families with **ing** and **d**.

> wrestle   wriggle   saddle   shuffle   paddle   struggle

5. Finish these sentences with the correct **ed** or **d** endings.

I paddle_____ down the river in a canoe.

We travel_____ to the beach.

We fill_____ our water bottles at the tank.

I buckle_____ the girth when I saddle_____ the horse.

We shovel_____ the sand as we tunnel_____ on the beach.

Making plurals

Some words add **s** or **es** to make plurals, like this:

present – **present<u>s</u>**
box – **box<u>es</u>**

Other words change their spellings altogether.

For example: **man** – **men**

6. Write the plurals of these words in your workbook.

> woman   man   mouse   foot   louse
>
> tooth   child   leaf   goose

Name

Sounds the same

 Homophones are words that sound the same but have different spellings. **Know** and **no** are homophones.

1. Cross out the *incorrect* homophone in these sentences.

I know/no that we are going to be to/too late to catch the plane/plain.

I hope there/their uncle will give us a lift to the airport.

2. Read these sentences aloud. Then complete them by using the correct homophone from the box underneath. Complete the title too. If you are not sure of any words, check the meaning in your dictionary.

_____day fun

We went _____ my uncle's farm on my _____day.

It is _____ kilometres from _____.

We had a _____ time. We watched my

uncle _____ wheat. Then we _____

on the tractor and had _____ _____ for lunch.

Birth/Berth	two/too/to	birth/berth	fore/four/for
hear/here	grate/great	sew/so/sow	some/sum
	road/rode	steak/stake	

 Continued on P39

Name

Continued from P38

Where and **were** sound alike – unless you make an effort to sound the **h** in **where** (and this may help you to spell **where**).

Were is a verb. It shows that something happened in the past.
Were is used with **we, you** and **they**.
For example: We **were** out yesterday.

3. Complete these sentences, using **where** or **were** to fill the gaps.

We _____ going to his party.

I knew you _____ being silly.

We _____ jumping off the step.

_____ are you going on Tuesday?

Is this _____ the party is being held?

Our means that something belongs to us.
For example: This is **our** house.

Are is a verb. For example: We **are** late.

Or usually means there is a choice.
For example: I will come on Sunday **or** Monday.

Our, are and **or** sometimes sound similar, so say them carefully to help you to hear the differences.

4. Say these sentences aloud, using **our, are** or **or** to fill in the spaces. Then complete the sentences with the correct words.

They _____ coming to _____ house on my birthday.

What would you like for your birthday? A box of chocolates _____ a new bike?

I think you would like _____ new car. It is a Rolls Royce!

Where _____ friends? _____ they coming _____ not?

Name

| field | brief | ceiling |
| receive | friend | |

| height | weight | eight |
| seize | their neighbour | |

| warm | dwarfs | swarm |
| towards | quarter | |

| crawled | awful | prawn |
| sawn | hawk | |

| straw | paw | drawer |
| beach | shore | |

| sharp | sprinkled | salmon |
| mathematics | Keith jumped off | |

Look at these words.

Say them aloud.

Cover each set of words.

Write them in your workbook.

Check to see if you are right.

When you have written each set of words, CHECK them to see if they are right. If they are right, put a tick. If any are wrong, cross them out. Look carefully at the correct word(s) again, note where you went wrong and write them again in your wordbank.

There are 33 words. How many did you get right first time?

 Continued on P41

Name

1. They watched him leap off the train as it was moving.

2. Her friend noticed that the dolphin had hurt its mouth.

3. The men signalled to their friends.

4. She thought they were struggling to get free.

5. The women had travelled many miles with their children.

6. I know that you will be too late to reach the airport in time.

7. I thought we could have a wonderful time on our birthdays.

8. We threw the ball to her and she caught it at once.

9. Dad asked, "Why are you crying?"
   "I have something in my eye," I replied.

10. The science room seems to be full of scissors and funny scents!

Look at these words.

Say them aloud.

Cover each set of words.

Write them in your workbook.

Check to see if you are right.

Do the same with these sentences. (Don't forget to look at the punctuation!) You can WRITE, then CHECK after each sentence.

How many sentences were correct?

Enter any words that were not correct into your wordbank under the correct letter. Do this even if the word is there already.

Name

Objective: Spell words with the long *o* sound as in *boat*.

Unit 7

Christmas list

1. Read this story aloud. Then underline all the words with the long **o** sound.

At Christmas

There are a few things that I'd like for Christmas. I've asked Santa for a boat – a model of a coastal steamer. I saw one I liked in a shop in Okehampton. I need a new coat and Mum said that Grandma wanted to get me one. I think I groaned when she said that. My brother wants a frog that croaks.

2. Make these **oat** words and write them on the lines.

b
c
fl
g
m
thr

oat

_____

_____

_____

_____

_____

3. Write four sentences of your own using **oa** words.

_____

_____

_____

_____

Objectives: Spell words with the long *o* sound as in *boat*. Spell plurals and *tion* words.

Continued from P42

Unit 7

4. **Boat** rhymes with **coat**. Write the words which rhyme side by side in your workbook.

boast	coax	hoax	toad	coal	coast
groan	road	moan	moat	float	shoal

5. Write the plural of each of these words. Some will be spelled with **s**, **es**, **ies** or **ves**. Be careful! Some plurals are *the same* as the singulars.

cloak _____   groan _____   loaf _____

reply _____   bus _____   coach _____

toad _____   baby _____   sheep _____

knife _____   soap _____   salmon _____

6. Read these **tion** words aloud.

inspec**tion**	educa**tion**	sta**tion**
dic**tion**ary	informa**tion**	atten**tion**

7. Now use the **tion** words you have just read to complete these sentences.

The s_____ office will give you i_____ about train times.

I used a d_____ to help me to spell e_____.

I hope you will all pay a_____ when we have

an i_____.

8. Circle the **tion** part of the words you have written in the sentences.

A to Z

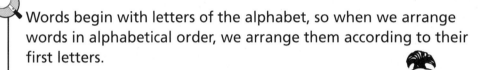

Dictionaries are arranged in alphabetical order. That means the **Aa**s come first, followed by the **Bb**s, **Cc**s, **Dd**s and so on until we get to the **Zz**s.

1. Write all the letters of the alphabet in alphabetical order on a piece of paper. Use capital and small letters. Write them like this: **Aa**, **Bb**…

Words begin with letters of the alphabet, so when we arrange words in alphabetical order, we arrange them according to their first letters.

These words are in alphabetical order:
arm, **book**, **fossil**, **noon**, **see**, **zoo**.

Their first letters are **a**, **b**, **f**, **n**, **s** and **z**.

2. Arrange these words in alphabetical order. Then put them in your wordbank.

| Christmas | Easter | wedding | birthday | Britain | festival |

_____   _____

_____   _____

When you arrange words alphabetically, it doesn't matter if a word has a capital letter or not. Capital letters tell us about proper nouns and make no difference to alphabetical order.

Sometimes, words begin with the same letter of the alphabet. For example: **ace**, **afraid**, **answer**, **arm**, **attack**. To put them into alphabetical order we go to the *second* letter. The second letter of each word above is **c**, **f**, **n**, **r** and **t**. As these letters are in alphabetical order, so the words are too.

3. In your workbook, write these words in alphabetical order, then put them in your wordbank. Remember to Look–Say–Cover–Write–Check each word into your wordbank.

fungus	fudge	football	field
frog	famous	floppy disk	

4. Say these words aloud. Write them out in alphabetical order in your workbook.

something	spaceship	snuggle	
slide	sausage	seldom	scream

5. If any of the words are new, add them to your wordbank.

Sometimes the first two letters in words are the same. If this happens, you have to look at the *third* letter to place the words in alphabetical order. For example: in the words **chicken** and **Christmas**, the **i** in **chicken** comes before the **r** in **Christmas** in the alphabet. Therefore, you would find chicken before Christmas in your dictionary.

6. Say these words aloud. Then arrange them in alphabetical order in your workbook.

done	dome	doze	dog
ham	handle	hard	have

7. Add them to your wordbank. Don't just copy them! Use Look–Say–Cover–Write–Check.

8. Now do the same with these words. Check the meanings of any words that are new to you.

ice	fit	arm	does	illness	fine
me	men	apple	serviette	stoat	

Name

Objective: Spell words with *au* making the *aw* sound, as in *cause*.

Unit 9

Special festivals

When **au** is in the middle of a word, it often has an **aw** sound, like **cause**. **Because** also has a similar sound.

1. Read aloud these statements about favourite festivals. Underline all the words with the **aw** sound.

CATHY: I like Christmas when all the family is together and there are baubles on the tree.

CAROLE: I like Easter because I like going to church and seeing the flowers on the altar. If I'm not naughty, I'm given an Easter egg.

MARIE: I like St Patrick's Day (17 March), because I was born on that day. I'm being taught Irish dancing. The applause afterwards is great!

SHAUN: My Dad is called David. Last year on St David's Day (1 March), we caught a train to go to Cardiff, so that's my favourite day.

2. Say each of these words aloud. Listen for the **aw** sound.

clause	autumn	fraud	haul
launch	sauce	exhaust	saucer

3. Look at each word and then cover it. Now write each word in your wordbank. Check!

Objective: Put words in alphabetical order, using the third and fourth letters.

Continued from P46

🔍 Remember that words are in alphabetical order in a dictionary.

4. In what order would these words come in your dictionary? Write them in dictionary order. Hint: the first word is **candle**.

Christmas   candle   cycle   clay   crystal   clown

_____

_____

5. Do the same with these words. You will need to go to the *third* letter in each word to work out the dictionary order. Read them *aloud* first.

Christmas   champagne   cry   chicken   crumble

crayfish   chop   creek   crow

_____

_____

_____

6. Now go to the *fourth* letter and arrange these words in dictionary order.

strike   stray   stroll   street   strength

_____

_____

6. This will test you! In what order would you find these words in a dictionary? Write them in order, then check your answer in a dictionary.

Christmas   christen   Christ

_____

Name

Keep your shirt on

1. Read this text aloud. Underline the **ar** words as in **car** sound.

March days

St Patrick is the patron saint of Ireland. We celebrate St Patrick's Day on 17 March. On that day we march in the parade which finishes in the park. There's always a good party in the park.

   My mum's birthday is on 14 March. Her name is Margaret. This year on her birthday we went by car to a special market. Mum bought jars of peaches and four apple tarts.

 ir and **ur** often sound similar.

2. Read this poem aloud and underline the **ir** and **ur** words.

Keep your shirt on

The tiger has a shirt of fur,
The bird has one of feather,
The fish's shirt keeps out the rain
In all the wettest weather.
But my outside is not like theirs,
As I have had to learn:
My skin cannot keep out the cold
And in the sun I burn.
But even if my skin were thick,
And I were so disposed,
The word is that it's not the thing
To take off all your clothes.
I've heard that people must not be
Indecently exposed.
The tiger keeps his shirt on, too,
As everybody knows.

Gordon Winch

Photocopiable ▪ SCHOLASTIC Continued on P49

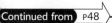
3. Write any new words from the last page in your wordbank. Remember to Look–Say–Cover–Write–Check.

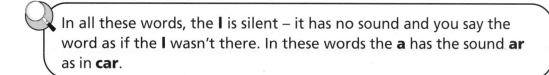

In all these words, the **l** is silent – it has no sound and you say the word as if the **l** wasn't there. In these words the **a** has the sound **ar** as in **car**.

4. Say these silent **l** words aloud. Check the meanings of any words new to you. Then write the words.

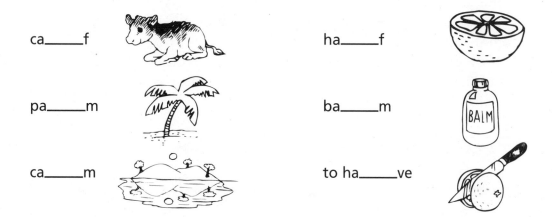

ca_____f

pa_____m

ca_____m

ha_____f

ba_____m

to ha_____ve

5. Use the silent **l** words you made above in these sentences.

We sat under the _____ tree.

After the fireworks festival, the night was _____.

I've cut the orange into two pieces; _____ for me and _____ for you.

The cow gave birth to a baby _____.

You should watch much less TV. Why don't you _____ the time you watch it?

My back was sore so I put some _____ on it to make it feel better.

Objective: Spell words with the *s* sound as in *cell*, *receive* and *face*.

 Unit 11

Cinderella the celebrity

1. Read this silly story.

Cinderella the celebrity

Cinderella celebrated by going to the ball. The ball was held at the Civic Centre which was next to the Civic Cinema. The Citizen's Ball was a bit of a circus. But it didn't cost Cinderella a penny to go and she was certain she would meet her prince there.

She did meet him, in spite of her ugly sisters, Lucy and Dulcie. And how gracefully she danced when she received an invitation from the prince!

But soon twelve o'clock came and she had to run. As she raced out of the place, she lost one of her glass slippers. Her face turned red with shame.

In many of the words in the story, **c** is followed by **e**, **i** or **y**. When this happens the **c** has the **s** sound.

2. Underline all the **c** words with an **s** sound. Write any new words in your wordbank.

3. Here are some more **c** words with the **s** sound. Write them in your wordbank. Remember to Look–Say–Cover–Write–Check!

dance	pencil	fancy	advance	decide
cycle	December	excite	bicycle	

Photocopiable ◼ S C H O L A S T I C Continued on P51

Name

Objective: Use *dis*, *mis* or *un* prefixes and *er* or *or* suffixes.

Continued from P50

Unit 11

4. Change the meanings of these sentences by adding **dis**, **mis** or **un** to the words in bold.

I _____**understood** what you said.

The sailor _____**furled** his flag.

He _____**agreed** with me.

I think I'll have the gas service _____**connected**.

Princess Anne is _____**interested** in horses.

5. Write down the meanings of these words. The first one has been done for you.

printer   *a person who prints* _____

teacher   _____

farmer   _____

actor   _____

author   _____

 Words that end in **er** or **or** refer to a person doing the word: a printer prints, an actor acts.

You will have to learn whether the suffix is **er** or **or**. These suffixes are the tricky part of the word.

6. Here is a list of **er** and **or** words. Sort them into **er** and **or** words and write two lists in your workbook.

baker	survivor	cricketer	explorer	instructor	mayor
gardener	traitor	minister	traveller	conductor	miner
employer	governor	lawyer	sculptor	spectator	

7. Learn each word by using Look–Say–Cover–Write in your wordbank. Don't forget to check!

Name

Objectives: Spell irregular verbs. Build compound words with *where, one, thing* and *body.*

Unit 12

I see, I saw

 Irregular verbs change their spelling when used in the past tense.

For example: I **see** – I **saw** – I **have seen**

1. Here are some irregular verbs. Write their past-tense spellings. The first one has been done for you.

I drive   *I drove*   *I have driven*

I break   _____

I draw   _____

I eat   _____

I fall   _____

2. Underline the correct form of the words in brackets to complete these sentences.

Yesterday I (forget/forgot) to feed the dog.
I (give/gave) a present to Mum last week.
I (know/knew) I was right.
I (ride/have ridden) six kilometres to be here today.
I used to (speak/spoke) very quickly when I was nervous.

 We often join two words to make one new word called a compound word. We spell the new word by being able to spell the two little words that make it up.

little words   **compound word**
every where   everywhere

3. Write the compound words for these little words in your workbook. Don't forget the second **e** in **every**.

every one   every thing   every body

Name

Continued from P52

The letter **c** sometimes has a soft **s** sound when it is followed by **e**, **i** and **y**.

For example: **face**

In the same way, the letter **g** has a soft **j** sound when it is followed by **e**, **i**, or **y**.

For example: **cage**

4. Say these soft **g** words aloud, then write them *from memory* into your wordbank.

village	garage	cottage	cabbage	huge	gymnasium
gigantic	gin	giraffe	tragic	magic	gymnastics
Egypt	biology	energy	giant	gypsy	

5. Use some of the soft **g** words to complete these sentences.

We went to the gymnasium to practise our _____.

The country _____ had lovely rose trees in its garden.

He was so tired that he hardly had the _____ to undress for bed.

Mum took her car to the

_____ to be repaired.

Name

Look at these words.

Say them aloud.

Cover each set of words.

Write them in your workbook.

Check to see if you are right.

boat	coast	coastal
groaned	croaked	
throat	boast	knife/knives
inspection	education	
dictionary	attention	famous
sausage	does/doesn't	
because	applause	clause
fraud	autumn	
naughty	Christmas	parade
park	shirt	
fur	burn	calf
half	circus	

When you have written each set of words, CHECK them to see if they are right. If they are right, put a tick. If any are wrong, cross them out. Look carefully at the correct word(s) again, note where you went wrong and write them again in your wordbank.

There are 32 words. How many did you get right first time?

 Continued on P55

Name

1. We went to the dance in December even though we had not received an invitation.

2. They decided to cycle to school every day in February.

3. She unfurled the flag and hoisted it to the top of the flagpole.

4. The traveller gave the conductor his fare.

5. We saw the gardener putting lovely flowers everywhere in the cottage.

6. He spoke in a whisper, saying, "This is a land of magic, one where you will see giants and dwarfs."

7. At Easter I received a huge egg made of chocolate.

8. I knew I had caught a huge salmon when my fishing line broke.

9. They celebrated Christmas by inviting their family and friends to dinner.

10. He used up all his energy working-out in the gymnasium.

Look at these words.

Say them aloud.

Cover each set of words.

Write them in your workbook.

Check to see if you are right.

Do the same with these sentences. (Don't forget to look at the punctuation!) You can WRITE, then CHECK after each sentence.

How many sentences were correct?

Enter any words that were not correct into your wordbank under the correct letter. Do this even if the word is there already.

Name

Objective: Spell words with the long *o* sound as in *blow*.

Unit **13**

A wedding day

1. Read this story about a wedding. Take care with **bouquet** (sounds like **bookay**) and **aisle** (sounds like **I'll**).

Aunt Jane's wedding

Do you know my Aunt Jane? She's my mum's sister. Well, she was married on Saturday. She looked great. Her dress had a big bow at the back. You could see it as she walked down the aisle of the church really slowly. Her dress had long sleeves that came right past her elbows. The bridesmaids came first, and Aunt Jane followed them. She smiled at me as she walked past. I was sitting in the third row.

  After the wedding there was a party with speeches and dances. I watched Aunt Jane throw her bouquet to the ladies. Then Jane and her new husband Bill went off in their new yellow car. I like Bill.

2. Underline all the long **o** sounds. Write the words onto the cake.

3. In your workbook, write a short story about a real wedding or an imaginary one.

 Continued on P57

Name

Continued from P56

4. What are these phrases describing? Each answer has a long **o** sound. Write the words in your workbook.

opposite of high

cold, white flakes of _____

a rabbit lives in one

a black bird

to cut the lawn

opposite of above

you look out of one of these

opposite of wide

you wheel one of these

you cast one of these when you stand in the sun

5. Make these **o** words.

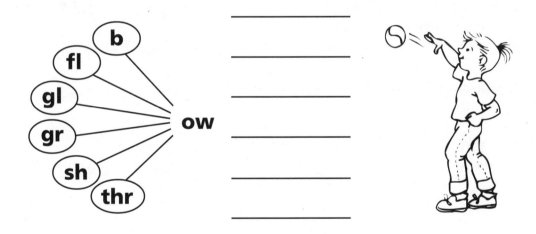

6. Use the words in the box below to finish this story. Write any new words in your wordbank.

> shadows   followed   slowly   narrow   own   glow   bellow

Jack let out a loud _____ and ran down the _____ lane.

The man _____ him part of the way and then walked back very

_____. Jack was on his _____ in the dim _____

of the street light which lit the_____ of the tall buildings.

Name

Auntie Jane's engagement

1. Read this poem aloud. Look out for words which have an **aw** sound in them.

Engagement party

Forty people, even more,
Seemed to come through every door;
Sat on chairs or on the floor.
Should have seen the clothes they wore
At Auntie Jane's engagement.

The noise was loud, a mighty roar,
A noise no neighbour could ignore.
They'd never heard such noise before.
We sang 'til we could sing no more.
At Auntie Jane's engagement.

Then the speeches. What a bore!
At last the food I'd waited for:
The cakes I really did adore;
I ate three apples to the core.
At Auntie Jane's engagement.

Gordon Winch

 'til is a contraction of **until**.

2. Now underline all the words in the poem that have an **aw** sound .

3. Find out the meanings of **ignore** and **adore** and write the words and definitions in your wordbank.

Continued from P58

Unit **14**

🔍 In **tion** words, the **ti** sounds like **sh** and so **tion** sounds like **shun**.

4. Read these **tion** words aloud, then, using Look–Say–Cover–Write–Check, put them in your wordbank. It may help you to spell the words if you split them into syllables. The first two have been split up for you.

sen sa tion	de cor a tion
education	separation
attention	invention
population	portion
consideration	

5. Now read these sentences and write the **tion** word from above which makes sense in each space.

The scientist created an _____ which could make wheels go round more quickly.

Some people are very thoughtless and have no _____ for others.

When my brother made the wedding cake, he put a silver

_____ on it.

The twins hated the long _____ from each other.

Name

Objectives: Spell words with final consonant blends with *t* and *d*. Use words ending in *ture*.

Wedding celebrations

1. Read this story aloud, finishing the words with **st**, **nt** or **nd**.

Sailing party

You ju_____ mu_____ hear about my Mum and Dad and their wedding anniversary.

It was the be_____ day. We we_____ out on our frie_____'s

boat, the one with the tall ma_____. It goes really fa_____ when the

wi_____ blows and this was a very wi_____y day. Did the ma_____

ever be_____? It be_____ so much that the boat was on a sla_____.

We would have been fir_____ if it had been a race.

2. Write the words in your wordbank.

 ture at the end of words sounds like **chur** or **chir**.

3. Say each of these **ture** words aloud, then write them in your wordbank from memory. Underline the **ture** part.

picture	adventure	denture	fixture	puncture
lecture	mixture	furniture	capture	

4. Check the meanings of any words new to you. Now write some sentences of your own in your workbook, using six of the **ture** words.

  Continued on P61

Continued from P60

5. Read this story aloud.

6. Write all the **c** and **ck** words from the story in your wordbank. It may help to remember that most (but not all) of the words of *one* syllable end in **ck**. Words of *more than one* syllable usually end in **c**.

Objective: Spell words containing *gh*.

The wonderful person of Sparta

A limerick is a rhythmic nonsense poem containing five lines.
Lines 1, 2 and 5 rhyme, and lines 3 and 4 rhyme.

1. Read this limerick by Edward Lear.

> There was an old person of Sparta,
> Who had twenty-five sons and one daughter.
> He fed them on snails
> And weighed them in scales,
> That wonderful person of Sparta.

2. Underline **daughter** and **weighed**. Both these words have a silent **gh**. This makes them tricky to spell, so look at them carefully. Write them in your wordbank.

3. Here are some more silent **gh** words. Say them aloud.

caught	taught	thought	through	weigh
neigh	height	sleigh	plough	though
	although	thorough	bough	

4. See how many of the words above you can write from memory into your wordbank. Remember to check!

Photocopiable ■ SCHOLASTIC Continued on P63

Objective: Spell and make contractions of *not*.

Continued from P62

Unit **16**

🔍 **Isn't** is short for **is not**.

5. Read these words. They are contractions from **not**. Write the full form on the lines next to them.

don't _____   won't _____

didn't _____   aren't _____

couldn't _____   doesn't _____

wasn't _____   shouldn't _____

hasn't _____   mustn't _____

wouldn't _____

6. Write out these sentences in your workbook, making all the words in bold into contractions with **not**.

> It **is not** the first wedding I have been to.
> I **do not** remember the first one.
> I **have not** been to many, though.
> Jake likes weddings, but he **would not** do what I told him.

7. Make the following phrases into *opposites*, using contractions of **not**. The first one has been done for you. The secret is to think about adding **not** to each one, but writing it as a contraction. Be careful with **can**.

I did *I didn't* _____   I was _____

I do _____   they can _____

I have _____   you are _____

I could _____   I am _____

he does _____   she will _____

Unique unicorn

If you know the meaning of the prefix of a word, it helps you to understand the word and spell it correctly. Here are some number prefixes and their meanings.

uni = 1	bi = 2	tri = 3	quad = 4	quin = 5
sex = 6	sept = 7	octo = 8	nov = 9	dec = 10
cent = 100				

A unicorn has **one** horn. A bicycle has **two** wheels.

1. Read these sentences, and write in the correct numbers.

A triangle has _____ angles.

A quadrilateral has _____ sides.

A quintet has _____ singers or players.

A sextet has _____ singers or players.

A septennial comes every _____ years.

An octopus has _____ arms (or legs).

November is our eleventh month but it was the _____ in the old Roman calendar.

With decimals you count in _____.

These prefixes come from Latin and Greek.

The Latin for **one** was **unus**; the Greek for **ten** was **deka**.

We do not *need* to know where the words came from in order to spell them, but it sometimes helps with the meanings as well as the spellings.

Name

Objective: Spell words with number prefixes.

Continued from P64

2. Finish these words, using the clues from the other sheet.

1 wheel	unicycle
2 wheels	_____cycle
3 wheels	_____cycle

after two years	_____ennial
after three years	_____ennial
after 100 years	_____ennial

4 singers	quartet
5 singers	_____tet
6 singers	_____tet
7 singers	_____tet

2 babies	twins
3 babies	_____plets
4 babies	_____ruplets
5 babies	_____tuplets

3 angles	_____angle
3 colours	_____colour
3-wheeled bike	_____cycle

3. Complete the months in their correct order.

September   _____ber   _____ber   _____ber

4. Do this quick quiz. Write the answers in your workbook. Turn this sheet upside down for the answers.

1. If a **biped** has two legs, how many legs has a **quadruped**?

2. Then, (a) what is a boy? (b) what is a dog?

3. How many singers are there in a **trio**?

4. How many rows of oars did a **quinquireme** have?

5. If **duplicate** is the word for two copies, what is the word for three?

Answers: 1. Four. 2. (a) Biped, (b) Quadruped; 3. Three; 4. Five; 5. Triplicate.

Wonderwords

You use your dictionary to check the spelling of a word or to find out its meaning. You find the word in the dictionary using what you know about alphabetical order. The first important thing is to know what each item on the dictionary page means.

Let us look at the word **birthday**.
This is how it appears as an entry in *My First Wonderword Dictionary*.

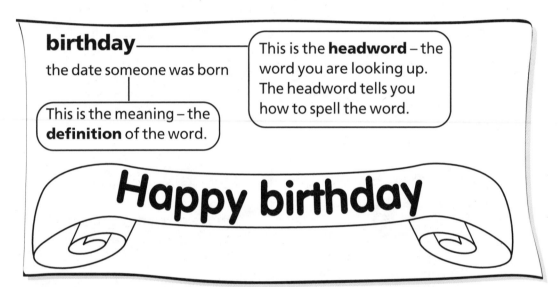

birthday
the date someone was born

This is the meaning – the **definition** of the word.

This is the **headword** – the word you are looking up. The headword tells you how to spell the word.

Happy birthday

Some dictionaries give the pronunciation (the way the word should be said), as well as the meaning.

For example: after **birthday** it might say *berth*–day.

1. Say **berth–day** aloud. It is in two syllables. The dash in between tells you this.

Remember, this is the way the word birthday is *said*. You know that the spelling is different.

Continued from P66

Some words have more than one meaning.
Here is the *My First Wonderword Dictionary* entry for the word **cross**.
There are three meanings:

cross
1. to move across something
2. a mark like this + or x
3. angry

2. Read these sentences aloud.

Put a cross beside your name.   ◯

I am feeling cross today.   ◯

Do not cross the road if the light is red. ◯

You sound very cross. What is the matter? ◯

That cross shows you where we are on the map. ◯

3. Think about the meaning of **cross** in each sentence and put **1**, **2** or **3** in the circle next to each one.

 Some dictionaries show other words from the same family.

4. Look at this word family of **brave**.

If you are **brave** you do things **bravely**, with **bravery**.

 Some dictionaries tell you interesting things about unusual words. Do you know what the word **billabong** means?

The dictionary says: **billabong** (*bil*–a–bong) (from **billa** meaning *river*; and **bong** meaning *dead*.)

Billabong is an Australian Aboriginal word and originally meant 'the branch of a river running to a dead end'.

Name

Look at these words.

Say them aloud.

Cover each set of words.

Write them in your workbook.

Check to see if you are right.

know/knew	elbow	bouquet
yellow	below	
bellow	shadow	narrow
barrow	door	
floor	adore	sensation
attention	portion	
education	population	first
mixture	fixture	
adventure	capture	frantic
panic	garlic	
even though	height	weight
through	triangle	

When you have written each set of words, CHECK them to see if they are right. If they are right, put a tick. If any are wrong, cross them out. Look carefully at the correct word(s) again, note where you went wrong and write them again in your wordbank.

There are 32 words. How many did you get right first time?

 Continued on P69

Name

Continued from P68

1. Their daughter is marrying the friend of my Uncle Keith.

2. You mustn't believe him, even though he said he was telling the truth.

3. He said the unicorn was riding a bicycle. What a fantastic story!

4. The babies were quins and the noise from the five of them was terrific.

5. She had a duplicate key made so that she could get into the office easily.

6. One wheel of the tricycle had a puncture, but Dad mended it quickly.

7. The definitions of what words mean can be found in your dictionary.

8. After the wedding, they celebrated by having a sensational party.

9. Somebody had broken their furniture. I wondered who had caused such damage.

10. My brother asked, "Are you coming to the wedding reception on Wednesday?" "No." I replied.

Look at these words.

Say them aloud.

Cover each set of words.

Write them in your workbook.

Check to see if you are right.

Do the same with these sentences. (Don't forget to look at the punctuation!) You can WRITE, then CHECK after each sentence.

How many sentences were correct?

Enter any words that were not correct into your wordbank under the correct letter. Do this even if the word is there already.

Name

Objective: Spell words with the *o* sound as in *go* and *toe*.

Going for gold

1. Read this text aloud.

School sports day

It was a very cold day. The rain was spitting down and the old stand didn't give much cover.

I had to run in the sprint and my teacher told me that the race would be before lunch. I strolled around until it was time for the start. My toe was hurting because it was a bit swollen. But I felt good.

We lined up for the start.

"Ready, set," said the starter and fired his starting pistol for 'go'.

I bolted off from the start and saw I was leading. "Gold, gold, gold," I was thinking.

2. Now underline the words that have the sound as in **go**.

3. Make words with the sound **o** as in **toe**, and write them in your wordbank. Check the meanings of any words new to you.

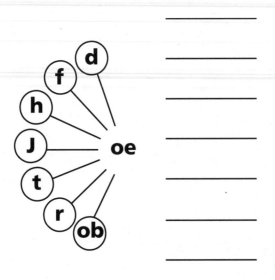

Photocopiable **SCHOLASTIC** Continued on P71

Name

Objective: Spell words with the *o* sound as in *go* and *toe*.

Continued from P70

Unit 19

We have studied words which follow the 'magic **e**' rule: **dot + e = dote**. Magic **e** makes **o** sound like its name.

If **o** is followed by a consonant and then another vowel in a word, it may also sound like its name.

c v c v c
For example: l **o** c a l

4. Say these words and listen to the **o** sound. Check the meanings of words new to you.

location	rotation	potato	social	Roman
provide	Romany	woven	total	sofa
sober	tomato	locate	rotate	solo

5. Now look, say, cover, and write the words in your wordbank. Remember to check the spellings and to look up the meanings of any new words.

6. Use the words in the box to complete the sentences below.

Roland   hose   local   motor   solar   froze

My uncle has a gnome named _____.

The _____ paper is delivered every Wednesday.

The _____ stopped and we had no paddles.

It was so cold, the water in the h_____ _____.

We have a _____ hot water system on the roof.

7. Write two sentences in your workbook about meeting Roland the gnome.

Name

Objectives: Revise plurals. Make plurals from words ending in *o*.

Unit **20**

Rhinos and hippos

When making more than one of something, we usually add an **s**.

For example: cat – cat**s**   vine – vine**s**

For words that end in s, ss, sh, ch or x, we usually add es.

For example: bu**s** – bus**es**   clas**s** – class**es**   bu**sh** – bush**es**
    chur**ch** – church**es**   fo**x** – fox**es**

For words that end in y, we change the y to i and add es.

For example: bab**y** – bab**ies**

1. Write the plural of each of these words.

Singular	Plural	Singular	Plural
chop	_____	brush	_____
beach	_____	witch	_____
berry	_____	fox	_____
cherry	_____	apple	_____
lass	_____	book	_____

Most words ending in **o** add **es** to make the plural.

For example: her**o** – hero**es**   tomat**o** – tomato**es**

Words that are abbreviations (that is, the *shortened forms* of the words) usually add **s** to make the plural.

Word	Abbreviation	Plural of abbreviation
pianoforte	piano	pianos
rhinoceros	rhino	rhinos
hippopotamus	hippo	hippos
kilogram	kilo	kilos
photograph	photo	photos

 Continued on   P73

Objective: Build words from onsets *scr*, *spr* and *str*.

Continued from P72

Unit **20**

2. Build new words from those below. Write them in your wordbank. The first one is done for you as an example of some of the ways in which this can be done.

scratch	stroke	sprinkle
scratches	_____	_____
scratched	_____	_____
scratching	_____	_____

3. Write **spr**, **scr** or **str** words that rhyme with the words below.

patch	scr_____	knew	scr_____
rung	spr_____	dribble	scr_____
paddle	str_____ .	pride	str_____
map	str_____	free	spr_____
stay	spr_____	length	str_____

4. Add any new words to your wordbank. Check their meanings too.

5. Read these sentences aloud, using **spr**, **scr** or **str** words that make sense. Complete the sentences.

He needs a great deal of str_____ to scr_____ the hook into the wood.

The giant began to str_____ towards the beanstalk.

My cat likes me to scr_____ her back.

I went on a shopping spr_____ with my brother.

My baby brother cannot write yet – he can only scr_____.

Sports training

 The prefix **fore** has the meaning **before**.

For example: **forehead** – that part of the head at the front

1. Draw lines to match the meanings with the words.

forearm   tell the future

forecast   the first part of the arm

forefathers   predict, for example the weather

foreground   at the front

foretell   grandfathers and great-grandfathers

foreword   the part of the book before the main text

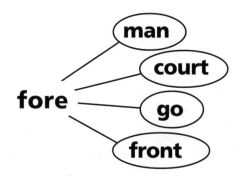

2. Complete these sentences, using the words **forehand**, **forecast** or **forewarned**.

Mr Davey _____ a win for our team today.

In tennis we play _____ and backhand strokes.

My coach _____ me about the slippery track.

3. Make four **fore** words and write them here.

_____

_____

_____

_____

fore

man

court

go

front

Objectives: Spell portmanteaux. Make plurals of words ending in *f* or *fe*.

Continued from P74

If we have a meal late in the morning, we have it between breakfast and lunch. We call this meal **brunch**. We take the two words: **breakfast** and **lunch** and make them into one word: **brunch.**

5. Make a common word from these groups of words.

smoke/fog _____

camera/recorder _____

motor car/hotel _____

airplane/bus _____

bedroom/sitting room _____

To make the plurals of words ending in **f**, the general rule is: change the **f** to **v** and add **es**. If a word ends in **fe**, change the **f** to **v** and ad **s**.

For example: lea**f** – lea**ves**

6. Make these singular **f** words plural.

Take care! Some of the **f** words do *not* follow the general rule.

calf _____   thief _____

shelf _____   dwarf _____

wolf _____   wife _____

knife _____   handkerchief _____

sheaf _____

7. Now write three sentences of your own in your workbook, using the plurals you have made.

Name

Shorten it

We can shorten words that we use very often. We use the words **street**, **road** and **Mister** very often, so we tend to use them in their shortened (abbreviated) forms.

1. Look at these shortened forms.

Usual shortened form	Full word
Mr	Mister
Rd	Road
St	Street

These contracted forms consist of the *first* and *last* letters of the full words.

For example: **M**iste**r** – **Mr**

For these contractions, no full stop is used to show the contraction.

2. Write these names in their abbreviated forms in your workbook.

Mister Thorpe   Doctor Smith

Father John   Sister Mary

Ellard Street   Forest Road

When a word is shortened by including part of the word but not the last letter, a full stop is often used to show the abbreviation.

For example: **Rev**erend – **Rev.**   **Capt**ain – **Capt.**

■ SCHOLASTIC Continued on P77

Objectives: Learn the conventions of letter-writing. Use abbreviations in context.

Continued from P76

Unit 22

3. Write these names in their abbreviated forms.

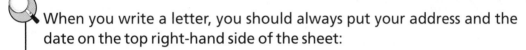

Major Campbell   Provost MacTeer   Colonel Singh

Professor Stanley   Admiral Lacey

4. Write any new words in your wordbank and check their meanings. Write the meanings next to the words.

When you write a letter, you should always put your address and the date on the top right-hand side of the sheet:

Your address

Today's date

5. Write a letter to Mister Hope in your workbook, one of your school governors, inviting him to the Sports Day at your school on Tuesday 3 July. The first race starts at 2.00pm, but ask him if he could be there for 1.30pm so that he can meet the competitors before he goes to his seat.

His address: 13 White Terrace, Little Sea, Stamfordshire, ST12 4PR. Write the letter, using the correct layout and abbreviations.

Finish your letter with:

Yours sincerely
(Write your name here.)

Remember to sign your name and then print it *clearly* beneath your signature!

6. Address an envelope to Mister Hope beneath the letter, using the correct layout and abbreviations.

Seeing the carnival

1. Here is a page from *My First Wonderword Dictionary*.
Let's find the word **carnival**.

---

capsule   29   **carpet**

---

capsule (*kap-shool*)
1 a very small container that has medicine powder inside it
2 the part of a spaceship where the astronauts sit at the controls

captain (*kap-tn*)
1 someone who is in charge of a ship or plane
2 someone who is in charge of a group of soldiers
3 any person who is in charge of other people

capture (*kap-cha*)
to grab someone or take control of something in a rough way
Word building: I *captured*, I am *capturing*, I'm *capturing*. Someone you capture is your *captive*

caramel (*ka-ra-mal*)
a light-brown sweet, made from sugar, butter and milk

caravan (*ka-ra-van*)
a van with windows and a door, that can be pulled along by a car. You can live in it when you are on holiday

card (*kahd*)
1 a piece of folded stiff paper or cardboard, with a picture on the front and writing inside, such as a birthday card or a Christmas card
2 one of a set of oblong pieces of cardboard with pictures on them. You use them for playing card games such as snap

cardboard (*kahd-bawd*)
a thick, stiff sort of paper

cardigan (*kahd-i-gun*)
a knitted jacket with buttons down the front

care (*kair*)
1 you care about something if it's important to you
2 you do something with care when you fix all your thoughts on it and give it your complete attention

Word building: I *cared*, I am *caring*, I'm *caring*. If you do things with care, then you are *careful*. If you don't do things with care and don't bother to think first, then you are *careless*

care for (*kair faw*)
look after
Word building: I *cared for*, I am *caring for*

cargo (*kah-goh*)
the goods carried on a ship or plane from one place to another
Word building: For more than one we use *cargoes*

carnival (*kah-na-val*)
1 sporting events held one after the other on a certain day: I'm going to watch my brother race at the carnival on Saturday
2 a special time when there are processions in the streets and people like to join in with dancing and singing

carol (*ka-ral*)
a happy Christmas song or hymn

carpenter (*kah-pen-ta*)
someone who makes things out of wood
Word building: The work of a carpenter is carpentry

carpet (*kah-pet*)
a thick cover for a floor. You weave it from

guide words

headwords

pronunciation guide

definition

The guide words on the page are **capsule** and **carpet**.
capsule is the *first* word entry on that page.
carpet is the *last* word entry on that page.
We have to use our knowledge of alphabetical order to understand that words on a page fall between our guide words that appear at the top of the page.

Guide words	Headwords	Will it be on that page?
capsule – carpet	captain	yes
	care	yes
	carnival	yes

2. In your workbook, write these words in alphabetical order.

square	sprinkle	bicycle	sprout
squirrel	blackbird	squid	buy
battery	sprint	bought	balloon

3. Add any new words to your wordbank. Use Look–Say–Cover–Write–Check.

4. If the set of headwords at the top of this page were the *only* entries on a page in a dictionary, what would be the guide words for that page?

_____   _____

5. If the guide words on a dictionary page are **classify** and **clip**, tick *yes* or *no* if the words listed should appear as a headword entry.

Word	Yes	No
dog		
game		
clear		
clay		
clinic		

Word	Yes	No
coach		
coat		
clever		
claw		
clap		

6. If the guide words on this dictionary page are **spit** and **spring**, tick *yes* or *no* if the words listed should appear as a word entry on the page.

Word	Yes	No
spit		
spite		
sport		
spin		
spell		

Word	Yes	No
spring		
spirit		
sprinkle		
spoil		

Name

Unit 24

Record breaker

1. Read this poem aloud.

It's lonely and nobody cares
I hope, hope, hope,
That I broke, broke, broke
The record that's stood for years.
I can't joke, joke, joke,
Can I cope, cope, cope?
It's lonely and nobody cares.

Gregory Blaxwell

2. Underline the **o** words in the poem. Note the **magic e**.

3. Write about winning or losing a race. Your story can be real or imaginary.

4. Make words with **o** as in **pope**, **coke** or **cove**. Write them in your wordbank.

ope c_____ p_____

oke c_____ p_____ st_____

ove st_____ dr_____

5. Make words using **ode**, **ole**, **one**, **ote**. Write them in your wordbank. Check the meanings of words new to you.

ode c_____ m_____ r_____

ole d_____ h_____ m_____ p_____ r_____ s_____

one b_____ c_____ l_____ t_____ z_____

ote n_____ d_____ v_____

Photocopiable ◀ SCHOLASTIC Continued on P81

6. You have used the **guide** words in a dictionary to help you to find words. Here are more **ui** words. Read them aloud and make sure they are in your wordbank. Check the meanings of any words you are unsure about.

juice

sluice

fruit

suit

recruit

guide

build

cruise

bruise

7. Use **ui** words to complete these sentences.

The army wants to r_____ more young people to train as soldiers.

Will I need a g_____ when I go walking in Scotland?

The channel that carries a fast current of water is called a

s_____.

My aunt went on a c_____ to America. She was at sea for three weeks.

After I fell downstairs, I had a huge b_____ on my arm.

Name

Look at these words.

Say them aloud.

Cover each set of words.

Write them in your workbook.

Check to see if you are right.

cold	bolted	toe/toes
swollen	potato	
tomato	provide	locate
social	rotate	
cherry/cherries	fox/foxes	piano/pianos
scratch	sprinkle	
forecast	foreground	motel
brunch	bedsit	
calf/calves	knife/knives	Dr Barrow
sincerely	dictionary	
guide	lonely	nobody
stove	build	

When you have written each set of words, CHECK them to see if they are right. If they are right, put a tick. If any are wrong, cross them out. Look carefully at the correct word(s) again, note where you went wrong and write them again in your wordbank.

There are 37 words. How many did you get right first time?

SCHOLASTIC Continued on P83

Name

Continued from P82

review Units 19–24

1. I strolled round the grounds before my race on Sports Day.

2. The location for our races was a field; no shelters were provided.

3. The witch hobbled over to the bushes and started laughing wickedly.

4. My photos of the churches turned out to be quite good after all.

5. Their bicycles had punctures so they telephoned their dad for assistance.

6. It is difficult to forecast what the weather will be.

7. If the airplane arrives on time, we will be permitted to have a guided tour of the airport.

8. She cried out, "I'm so lonely! I wish I could go on the cruise with the other children."

9. He spilt fruit juice down his favourite suit.

10. You can use a dictionary to find out the definitions and spellings of words.

Look at these words.

Say them aloud.

Cover each set of words.

Write them in your workbook.

Check to see if you are right.

Do the same with these sentences. (Don't forget to look at the punctuation!) You can WRITE, then CHECK after each sentence.

How many sentences were correct?

Enter any words that were not correct into your wordbank under the correct letter. Do this even if the word is there already.

Objective: Spell words with long *a* sounds, using *eigh*, *ea*, *ey* and *a*.

Unit 25

Animal park

> A long **a** sound, as in **change**, can also be spelled with **eigh**, **ea** and **ey**.

1. Read these words and listen for the long **a** sounds.

eight	grey	freight	prey	weight
taste	great	range	steak	pastry

2. Write the words in your workbook. Underline the long **a** sounds. Then look, say, cover and write the words again in your wordbank. Remember to check them!

3. Now listen to the long **a** sounds in this story.

A visit to an animal park

When my Australian cousins went to the animal park, they saw eight koalas asleep in a tree. Koalas eat gum leaves, which must taste terrible. How strange! I'd change my diet, wouldn't you?

The grey kangaroos were hopping about. They let my cousin pat them. They are quite big, but I don't know how many kilograms they weigh.

My cousins looked at the eagles, which are birds of prey. They eat small animals and birds. Many creatures in the bush prey on others. Koalas just eat gum leaves, and kangaroos just eat grass.

Afterwards, my cousins had a lunch break, with sandwiches, pastry and fruit to eat. They said it was great, and didn't waste a thing. It was better than leaves. What if they had eaten steak? Would they be 'birds of prey'?

4. Underline all the words with long **a** sounds.

5. Now sort these words into four sets in your workbook. One set of **eigh** words, one of **ea** words, one of **ey** words and one of **a** words.

 Continued on P85

Objective: Spell words with the *aw* sound, as in *caught* and *bought*.

Continued from P84

Words with an **aw** sound can be spelled **augh** or **ough**.

For example: **caught** and **bought**

6. Fill in the correct **aw** spelling for each word missing from this story.

Field trip

Our teacher t_____t us many things about animals, birds and plants on our excursion into the country.

We had br_____t our notebooks with us.

I th_____t it was a very interesting day.

Mark c_____t a frog but our teacher made him let it go.

Terry was n_____ty. He f_____t with Sarah.

Our teacher b_____t us a drink on the way home. It was a great excursion. You _____t to come too next time.

7. Use this word wheel to make an **ough** word family.

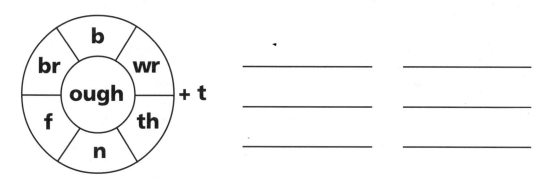

br, b, wr, f, ough, n, th + t

_____   _____

_____   _____

_____   _____

Do you know the meaning of **wrought**? Look it up in your dictionary.

8. Read these sentences aloud, filling in the **aw** words.

Her d_____ter c_____t a cold.

She t_____t me not to be n_____y.

Name

Objectives: Spell words with the prefix
ex. Use semicolons. Revise contractions.

Unit 26

Excellent skiers

This is a semicolon **;**. There is one at the end of the first line of each of the first three verses of this poem. They act a bit like a full stop, so you should pause when you come to one.

1. Read the poem aloud, pausing at all semicolons and full stops.

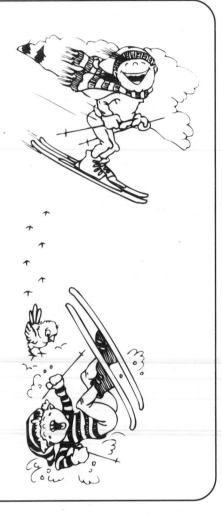

Skiing

I'm not good at skiing;
I always seem to fall.
It's hard when other kids all find
It's not so hard at all.

They're up and down the ski slopes;
You've seen their breakneck pace.
The way I creepy-crawl along
Is simply a disgrace.

We're off on an excursion;
It's next week when we go,
To find how birds and animals
Can live in all that snow.

I think that when I study them
I'll try to get it clear,
Why they're so good at standing up,
While I'm upon my rear.

Gordon Winch

2. Now write any two verses of the poem in your workbook. Take care with the punctuation and add drawings if you wish.

The prefix **ex** is from the Latin and Greek languages.

Ex means 'out of' or 'outside of'.

Photocopiable   ♠ S C H O L A S T I C   Continued on   P87

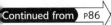

Objectives: Spell words with the prefix *ex*. Use semicolons. Revise contractions. Spell *sion* words.

Continued from P86

Unit **26**

3. Write these **ex** words in your wordbank and check their meanings.

> excursion   exhale   exit   extend   export   express

4. In your workbook, write three of your own sentences using **ex** words.

5. Look at the poem 'Skiing' again. Most of the contractions in the poem are in the present tense. That means they are happening now.

6. Write the contractions in your workbook. Next to them, write the words out in full.

7. Read these sentences aloud. Then write each sentence in your workbook, but write all the contractions *in full*.

> I'm going on an excursion to the snow. He's coming. She's coming too. They're all coming, in fact. It's going to be fun. We're hoping that you can come. Can you? They're all wanting to know.

 Excursion ends in **sion** (sounds like **shun**).

8. Read these **sion** words aloud and put any new ones in your wordbank.

> division   collision   provision   confusion   permission   persuasion

9. Now fill in the correct **sion** word in these sentences.

There was a _____ of feeling. Some children wanted to go to the fair; some wanted to go to the circus.

She obtained _____ to go to the disco.

The newspaper had a full report of the _____ on the motorway.

10. In your workbook, write two new sentences, using **sion** words.

Name

The maritime museum

Auto and anti

These parts of words have special meanings. If you know them, it helps you to spell the words and understand their meanings.

Auto comes from the Greek word *autos* meaning 'self' so an **autograph** is something you *write yourself*.

Anti comes from Greek, too. It means 'against' or 'opposed to', so an **antibiotic** is used *against nasty germs*.

1. Underline all the **auto** or **anti** words.

We went to the maritime museum. Kay Cottee, the lone sailor, was there. We bought her book about her life. It was her autobiography. She signed her autograph in it.

Then we went through the automatic doors onto the big warship. It had anti-aircraft guns on it.

Jamie Watts played up. Our teacher said he was being very antisocial.

2. Write the **auto** or **anti** words in your wordbank, then write what you think each word means. Use your dictionary to check your guesses.

Joke
Question: What kind of medicine do ants take when they are ill?
Answer: **Anti**biotics, of course!

3. Learn to spell the words in parts. Say and listen to these parts of words.

auto	●	graph
auto	●	biography
auto	●	matic
anti	●	social
anti	●	biotic

Name

Objective: Spell words containing the prefixes *auto*, *anti*, *ante* and *post*.

Continued from P88

4. Write the words in your workbook *without copying*. Check! If they are wrong, relearn them, and write them *again*.

5. Look–Say–Cover–Write–Check these words in your wordbank.

> antidote   automobile

6. Now fill the spaces in these sentences with words that make sense.

The doctor gave the boy an _____ when he was stung by the bee.

My dad has a new _____ which is bright red.

> **Ante** comes from Latin and means 'before'.
>
> **Post** comes from Latin, too. It means 'after'.
>
> **am** stands for **ante meridian** and means 'before midday'.
>
> **pm** stands for **post meridian** and means 'after midday'.
>
> We use **am** and **pm** instead of writing the whole phrases.

7. Read these sentences, filling in the spaces with the words given.

> pm   postpone   post-war

I had to _____ my visit until 6 _____ because I had to go out to lunch.

Food was still rationed in _____ Britain.

8. Now write the completed sentences in your workbook.

> Quiz question: What does **PS** mean at the bottom of a letter?
> Answer: 'Postscript' or 'written after'.

Rock pool excursion

Homophones are words which sound the same but are spelled differently and have different meanings. You can often tell which is the correct spelling of a homophone by thinking about the meaning of the word in a sentence.

1. Write this passage on the lines below, choosing the correct homophones. Use the sense of the sentences to help you choose.

Have you (bean/been) on an excursion to the rock pool? You can (sea/see) and (here/hear) all kinds of things.
    (Their/There) are crabs that scuttle under the weeds, and tiny fish swim (inn/in) and out with the (tied/tide).
    If you (weight/wait) quietly you will (see/sea) (so/sew/sow) much (more/moor). I watched the shellfish and anemones open (write/right) in front of my eyes. They (seamed/seemed) to forget that I was (their/there).
    The rock pool is a big (whole/hole) in the rock that is filled with water. It (seems/seams) to be a (hole/whole) world on its own.

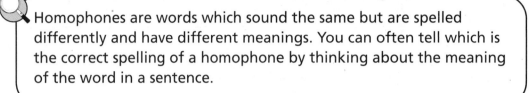

Words ending in **le** are very common but they *may* be tricky to spell because the **le** often sounds like **el** or **ul**. For example, **little** sounds as if it should be spelled as **littel**.

2. Read these **le** words aloud. Put any new words in your wordbank and check their meanings.

bottle   middle   muddle   meddle   ankle   bugle   spectacle

raffle   terrible   struggle   bundle   trifle   pebble   particle

3. The **t** in these **le** words is *silent*. Read the words aloud. Put any new words in your wordbank and check their meanings.

castle   whistle   rustle   jostle   bustle   thistle

4. Now arrange the words in alphabetical order, going across.

_____   _____   _____

_____   _____   _____

5. Write four sentences, or a short poem, using some **le** words.

_____

_____

_____

_____

_____

Where do words come from?

An etymological dictionary gives information about where words come from. Some *ordinary* dictionaries have etymological information too.

The information about where a word comes from is given after the word's meaning. Instead of using full words, abbreviations are used. Some common ones are: f. (from), F. (French), Sp. (Spanish), L. (Latin), G. or Gk. or Gr. (Greek), OE (Old English), It. (Italian), Turk. (Turkish).

1. Read these dictionary definitions of two words.

holiday – a period of vacation, a time when one is not at work (or school). It used to last only *one* day; it was a Holy Day. f. OE *halig daeg* meaning 'Holy Day'.
hippopotamus – large, short-legged, tusked, hairless animal living in water or rivers. f. Gk *hippos*, 'a horse', and *potamus*, 'a river'.

2. Underline the abbreviations used above, and write an explanation for each one.

_____

_____

_____

3. Some English words come from other languages. Read the following word definitions aloud. Look, say, cover and write each word in your wordbank. Check to see if you are correct.

siesta

a nap or rest in the early afternoon.
f. Sp. *sexta*, 'sixth', and *hora*, 'hour'.

Continued from P92 Unit 29

pasta

food made from a flour and
water dough. f. It. *paste*.

kayak

a light canoe. f. Inuit.

igloo

a dome-shaped Inuit hut. f.
Inuit *igdlu*, 'house'.

spaghetti

long strings of pasta. f. It. *spago*, 'a cord'.

shish kebab

grilled pieces of meat and vegetables
on a skewer. f. Turk. *sis*, 'skewer', *kebab*,
'roast meat'.

4. Write the words and definitions in your workbook.

5. Use an etymological dictionary to find out where these words come
from. Write out the words and their definitions.

anorak	pizza	yoghurt
video	baguette	

Name

Multiple meanings

 Some words have multiple meanings. This means there is more than one meaning listed for the word in the dictionary. You need to be careful to select the correct meaning.

1. Read this dictionary entry for the word **book**. It has two meanings.

> **book**
> **1** a number of pages fastened together with a cover, with words written for you to read
> **2** to order something in advance of when you need it

2. Which meaning is used in these sentences? Write the number **1** or **2** after each one.

I'm going to book the tickets for next week's show.

That is a very interesting book. You should read it. ◯

3. Write a sentence using meaning **1** and a sentence using meaning **2**.

_____

_____

_____

_____

4. Read this dictionary entry for the word **park**.

> **park**
> **1** a piece of land for people to use for pleasure
> **2** to place or leave your bicycle or car somewhere

 Continued on P95

Objective: Understand multiple meanings of words in a dictionary.

Continued from P94

5. Read these sentences. Which meaning of the word **park** is used in each sentence? Add the number **1** or **2** after each.

I'll park the car; you buy the tickets. ◯

I like the way they keep the gardens in this park. ◯

6. Write a sentence using meaning **1** and a sentence using meaning **2**.

_____

_____

_____

_____

7. This dictionary entry has *three* meanings. Read it aloud.

> **crawl**
> **1** to move along on one's hands and knees
> **2** to go very slowly
> **3** a way of swimming

8. Read these sentences. Which meaning of the word **crawl** would you use in each sentence? Add the number **1**, **2** or **3** after each.

He can do the crawl very well and should win the race. ◯

Our baby has learned to crawl. ◯

There was a traffic jam and the cars just seemed to crawl along. ◯

9. In your workbook, write your own sentences for meanings **1**, **2** and **3**.

10. Read these sentences showing two meanings of the word **cricket**.

> The cricket jumped like a grasshopper and made a funny noise. It had six legs.
> I like playing cricket with a real cricket ball and my dad's bat.

11. Write your own dictionary definitions for the word **cricket**.

Name

Look at these words.

Say them aloud.

Cover each set of words.

Write them in your workbook.

Check to see if you are right.

weight	eight	freight
change	range	
taste	caught	bought
thought	through	
exit	extend	express
excursion	collision	
division	confusion	autograph
automatic	antibiotic	
quietly	quite funny	their school
middle	bustle	
spectacle	holiday	spaghetti
pasta	yoghurt	

When you have written each set of words, CHECK them to see if they are right. If they are right, put a tick. If any are wrong, cross them out. Look carefully at the correct word(s) again, note where you went wrong and write them again in your wordbank.

There are 32 words. How many did you get right first time?

 Continued on P97

Name

1. It was great when we went on an excursion to animal park.

2. Many of them thought that the policeman had caught the thief.

3. They went skiing in February; it was quite a fantastic holiday.

4. Mum gave me permission to watch the television programme at 9.00pm.

5. The pop singer signed my autograph book; I was delighted, and smiled automatically.

6. She received a phone call from the doctor reminding her to take her antibiotics.

7. The little bottle was standing in the middle of the table.

8. For lunch we ate pizza, but for our evening meal we had spaghetti.

9. Your dictionaries may contain some very interesting information.

10. Their bicycles had punctures, but a friend of theirs repaired them.

Look at these words.

Say them aloud.

Cover each set of words.

Write them in your workbook.

Check to see if you are right.

Do the same with these sentences. (Don't forget to look at the punctuation!) You can WRITE, then CHECK after each sentence.

How many sentences were correct?

Enter any words that were not correct into your wordbank under the correct letter. Do this even if the word is there already.

Name

Objective: Spell words with the *oo* sound as in *bloom*.

Unit **31**

Show time

1. Read about the local show.

> ## Our local show
>
> The showground was ready and the gates would be opening soon. The flowers were all in bloom, the food had been brought in and the roofs of the buildings had been freshly painted. As it was Show Day, the local school was closed. At noon, the gates smoothly opened and the people zoomed in. There was plenty of room for everyone and all the farmers had cleaned their boots to come to the show.

2. Underline all the words with an **oo** sound.

3. Make **oo** as in **soon** words.

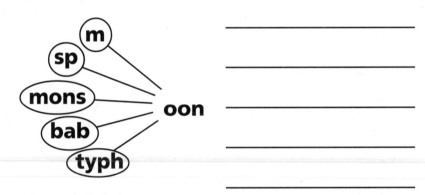

m
sp
mons
bab
typh

oon

_____

_____

_____

_____

_____

4. Put any new words in your wordbank. Check the meanings of any words you do not know.

5. Find the words that rhyme in this list and write them side by side in your workbook.

broom	roost	boost	goose	shoot
troop	loose	groom	scoop	root

6. In your workbook, write four sentences of your own, using **oo** words.

Photocopiable **SCHOLASTIC** Continued on P99

Objective: Spell words with *y* as in *happy* and *y* as in *multiply*.

Continued from P98

Unit **31**

7. Say **happy** and **multiply** aloud. Can you hear the short **i** sound in **happy**, and the long **i** sound at the end of **multiply**?

8. Say these **y** words aloud. Listen for the different sounds.

funny	reply	satisfy	family	python
tummy	mystery	sunny	qualify	terrify

9. Make two lists of those words – one for the short **i** sounds and one for the long **i** sounds.

_____   _____   _____

_____   _____

_____   _____   _____

_____   _____

10.   Read these sentences, filling in the spaces using **y** words that make sense. Write in the words.

Ten pancakes and a milkshake could not _____ his hunger.

The huge _____ slid along the branch; I was t_____ied that it would see me.

I did not _____ for the final of the marathon.

11. Write three sentences of your own, using **y** words.

_____

_____

_____

Name

Objective: Spell words with the *oo* sound as in *book*.

Unit **32**

All the fun of the fair

1. Read this list aloud and listen carefully to the **oo** sounds.

What I saw at the show:
wool from a merino sheep
wood-chopping
a clown with a hood on his head
someone cooking chips
a cow's horn shaped like a hook
a dog that never stood still
a good-looking book.

2. Underline all the **oo** words.

3. Make these **ook** words.

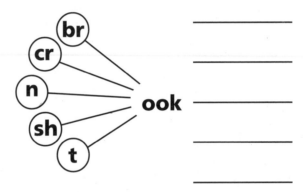

br
cr
n
sh
t
ook
_____
_____
_____
_____
_____

4. Make more **oo** words. Some of these words have a different, longer sound.

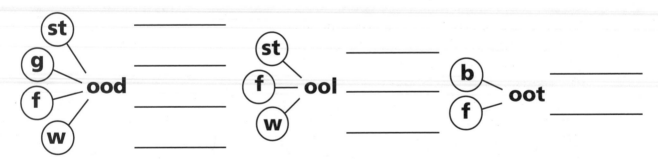

st
g
f
w
ood
_____
_____
_____
_____

st
f
w
ool
_____
_____
_____

b
f
oot
_____
_____

5. Write any new words on this page in your wordbank. Use Look–Say–Cover–Write–Check!

6. Some of the words have a long **oo** sound. Some have a short **u** sound. Sort them into two lists in your workbook. One list should be words that use the long **oo** sound, the other should contain words with the short **u** sound. Which list is longest?

Continued from P100

7. Read this poem aloud.

The Little Ghost's Song

I'd like to be human again.
I'd like to get wet in the rain.
I wouldn't mind toothache
Just for living's sake!
I'd like to get wet in the rain.
I'd like to be human again.
I'd like to kick a ball
And my foot not go through at all!
What's the good of being a ghost
If you can't eat jam and toast?
If you can't pull a funny face,
Or be sent to bed in disgrace?
I'd rather be scared than scare,
I'd like to breathe some air.
I'd like to get wet in the rain.
I'd love to be human again!

Brian Patten

8. Now read the poem again, pausing at all the full stops, question marks and exclamation marks.

9. The words **ghost** and **toothache** have a silent **h**. Underline these words in the poem.

10. Read these silent **h** words.

ghost	ghostly	ghastly
honest	honestly	hour
Thomas	River Thames	thyme

11. Write the silent **h** words in your wordbank and underline the silent **h** in each word. Check the meanings of any words you do not know.

Hear here

Homophones are words that have the same sound but a different spelling and meaning.

For example: **here** sounds the same as **hear**
It is always good to be **here**.
I can **hear** the bell.

1. Find homophones for these words. The first one has been done for you.

he'll	_heal_	_heel_
blew	_____	
to	_____	_____
there	_____	_____
know	_____	

2. Choose the correct words to use in these sentences and write the completed sentences in your workbook. If you're not sure of the meaning of a word, look it up a dictionary. Use the context of the sentence to help you.

The horses went to (there/their) watering (whole/hole).
The (rays/raise) of the (son/sun) touched the hills.
She (one/won) (for/fore/four) medals at the Show.
"He was last (seen/scene) heading across that paddock," said Mabel.
"Is that (sow/so)?" said Dad. "(I'll/aisle) (ring/wring) his neck when I catch him."
"It's just not (wright/write/right)," said Mabel.

Photocopiable **SCHOLASTIC** Continued on P103

Name

Objective: Revise homophones.

Continued from P102

3. Read this little story aloud.

The local show

The local show goes on for four **daze**. Everyone is **court** up in the activities. The best day is the last day; we always go **their** on the last day. There are fireworks on that day and they make a wonderful **seen**. I **sore** them last year **to**.

4. Write out the story, changing all the **bold** words to homophones that make sense.

5. Write sentences of your own to show the meanings of these four pairs of homophones.

rode   road

_____

_____

missed   mist

_____

_____

sore   saw

_____

_____

brake   break

_____

_____

Olympic history

1. Read this information aloud.

The Olympic Games

The first Olympic Games were held in Greece more than 2700 years ago. There was only one race in those games and that was a race of one lap of the track. It was one 'stade' in length. A 'stade' was a Greek measurement of about 184 metres. From this word, we get our word **stadium**.

Olympic Games are held every four years. They are terrific events.

2. **Olympic** and **tragic** both end in **ic** and not **ick**. Put these words, and other words from the passage that end in **ic**, in your wordbank.

3. Here are some more words ending in **ic**. Look at the words, say them, cover them, then write them in your wordbank *from memory*. Remember to check! Look up the meanings of any words you do not know.

panic	picnic	attic	horrific
tragic	topic	rustic	fantastic

Name _____

Continued from P104 ▷

4. Write these full words and the contractions on a piece of paper.

> I will – I'll   he will – he'll   we will – we'll   you will – you'll
> she will – she'll   it will – it'll   they will – they'll

5. Write these homophones and **will** contractions in your wordbank.
Check the meanings of any words that are new to you.

> I'll – aisle
>
> he'll – heel – heal
>
> we'll – wheel

🔍 Homophones are words that have the same sound but different
spellings and different meanings.

6. Write sentences of your own in your workbook, using these words.

> I'll   aisle   he'll   heel
>
> heal   we'll   wheel

7. Rewrite this story, choosing the correct homophone from the
brackets.

> The (we'll/wheel) fell off the cart. "Never mind," said Dad, "(we'll/
> wheel) soon fix it."
>   "(I'll/aisle) go and get some help," said Mum. "Oh dear. The (heel/
> heal/he'll) of my shoe has broken."
>   "Bob and Janice will be going down the (I'll/aisle) just about
> now," said Aunt Bessy. "(We'll/wheel) miss the wedding."
>   "It can't be helped," said Dad. "(We'll/wheel) get there as soon as
> we can."

Scuba diving

Many words come into our language because, originally, they were the first letters of words that describe an object or process. The word **scuba** is such a word and stands for:

s self
c contained
u underwater
b breathing
a apparatus

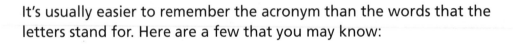

The word **scuba** is called an **acronym**.

It's usually easier to remember the acronym than the words that the letters stand for. Here are a few that you may know:

la – light amplification by

laser　**s** – stimulated

er – emission of radiation

ra – Radio

radar　**d** – Detection

a – And

r – Ranging

N – North

NATO　**A** – Atlantic

T – Treaty

O – Organisation

Name _____

Continued from P106   Unit 35

1. Write the acronyms from the last page in your wordbank, together with the words they stand for.

2. Draw lines to match these acronyms to the words they come from.

AWOL   Very Important Person

ASH   Compact Disk Read Only Memory

CD-ROM   Absent Without Leave

VIP   Action on Smoking and Health

3. Write these acronyms in your workbook and find out what they stand for.

> sonar   UNESCO   RAM   OPEC

4. Choose from the acronyms in this unit to finish these sentences.

The _____ divers could not find the wreck.

_____ is a valuable part of the United Nations.

Police often use _____ traps to detect speeding cars.

I just bought a new game on _____ for my computer.

5. Can you make up some acronyms of your own?

> For example:
> A **swip** is **s**omeone **w**ho **i**s **p**erfect.
> **NASTY** is the **Na**tional **S**ociety for **T**errible **Y**oungsters.

_____

_____

Spellcheck

What can dictionaries do?

Dictionaries tell you about words and give you their meanings. To find a word in the dictionary, you have to know how to spell at least the beginning of that word, otherwise you can't find it.

So, as far as spelling is concerned, a dictionary is often used to *check* your spelling, especially if words begin with silent letters, like **knock** and **honest**.

How to check spelling

Suppose you had to check the spelling of the word **parliament**. (Remember you don't know how to spell the word.)

1. Say the word. The beginning seems to be **par** or **parl**.
2. Look up **par** or **parl** in your dictionary until you come to a word that seems to be the one you are looking for.
3. Make sure it is the word you want by looking at the meaning.
4. In this case, you will find that the word is spelled **parliament**.
5. Now ask, "What is the hard part of the word?" The answer usually is that we don't say the **i**, so we might leave it out.
6. Look, say, cover and write the word in your wordbank. Check to make sure you can spell the word.

1. Write a sentence using **parliament**.

_____

_____

Continued from P108

2. Use your dictionary to check the spellings of some words. Go through this process.

> 1. My guess at spelling the first word is **favorit**. (This may not be the correct spelling.) It means 'liked the most'.
> 2. Write the first three letters you would look up in the dictionary.
> 3. What would you expect the next letter to be?
> 4. Now look in your dictionary. Make sure that you have found the correct word by writing down the meaning given in the dictionary.
> 5. Write the correct spelling of the word in your wordbank.
> 6. Underline the tricky part.

3. Use your dictionary to check the spelling of these words and write them correctly in your wordbank.

temprature
anythink
picknick
giraf (a tall African animal with a long neck)
ocupashon (job or hobby)
pronownse (to say a sound or word in a certain way)

4. Write sentences using these words.

_____

_____

_____

_____

_____

_____

_____

_____

Name

Look at these words.

Say them aloud.

Cover each set of words.

Write them in your workbook.

Check to see if you are right.

bloom	noon	baboon
typhoon	family	
python	terrify	terrified
reply	replied	
mystery	hood	stood
foot	shook	
ghost/ghostly	honest	Thomas
I'll/aisle	raise/rays	
brake/break	panic	horrific
Olympic	stadium	
organisation	society	action
apparatus	parliament	

When you have written each set of words, CHECK them to see if they are right. If they are right, put a tick. If any are wrong, cross them out. Look carefully at the correct word(s) again, note where you went wrong and write them again in your wordbank.

There are 34 words.
How many did you get right first time?

Continued from P110

review Units 31–6

1. I hope I do not lose my tickets to the show.

2. He was terrified when the huge python slithered down the tree and moved towards him.

3. She had an enormous meal of spaghetti for her lunch, but her hunger wasn't satisfied.

4. We stood in the pouring rain for eight hours before we had permission to go into the show.

5. Honestly, Thomas, I did not receive the photograph that you sent when on holiday.

6. The referee hoped to prevent confusion during the match.

7. The teacher thought that we could change our topic work on Wednesday.

8. I hear that our local MP is to come here to open the gala.

9. The opening of Parliament takes place in November; it makes a colourful scene on television.

10. When I was ill, I had a high temperature; the doctor whispered to Mum, "I'll give her some antibiotics."

Look at these words.

Say them aloud.

Cover each set of words.

Write them in your workbook.

Check to see if you are right.

Do the same with these sentences. (Don't forget to look at the punctuation!) You can WRITE, then CHECK after each sentence.

How many sentences were correct?

Enter any words that were not correct into your wordbank under the correct letter. Do this even if the word is there already.

word**bank**

Aa	arm	bedsit	body	brook
abbreviation	arrow	been	bold	broom
abroad	ASH	before	bolted	brought
action	ate	believe	bone	bruise
actor	attention	bellow	book	brunch
Adm.	attic	below	books	brush
Admiral	author	bend	boor	brushes
adore	autobiography	bent	boost	buffaloes
advance	autograph	berries	boot	bugle
adventure	automatic	berry	border	build
airbus	automobile	best	bore	bundle
aircraft	award	bicentennial	bottle	buoy
aisle	awful	biceps	bough	burn
although	AWOL	bicycle	bought	burrow
and		biennial	bouquet	bus
ankle		billabong	bow	bust
anorak	**Bb**	bind	bowl	bustle
antenatal	baboon	binoculars	boy	buy
ante-room	baby	biology	brake	
antibiotic	baguette	biped	brave	
antibiotics	baker	bird	bravely	**Cc**
antics	balloon	birthday	bravery	cabbage
antidote	balm	black	brawl	calendar
antiseptic	band	blackbird	break	calf
antisocial	barrow	blew	bridal	calm
anything	bats	bloom	bridle	calves
applause	battery	blue	brief	candle
apple	beach	board	Britain	capsule
apples	beaches	boarder	broad	Capt.
Arctic	bean	boast	broke	Captain
aren't	because	boat	broken	capture

■SCHOLASTIC Continued on P113

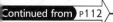

Continued from P112

wordbank

caramel	Christmas	convey	**Dd**	drew
caravan	circus	cook	dance	drove
card	clap	cooking	dawn	duck
cardboard	clause	cope	deceive	duplicate
cardigan	claw	coral	December	dust
care	clay	core	decide	dwarf
cargo	clear	cosmonaut	decimals	dwarfs
carnival	clever	cottage	deck	
carpenter	click	cough	decoration	
carpet	clinic	couldn't	deer	**Ee**
castle	cloak	crawled	denture	Easter
caught	clock	crayfish	dictionary	eat
CD-ROM	clothes	creak	didn't	eaten
ceiling	cloud	creek	disco	education
centennial	clown	Cres.	disposed	Egypt
champagne	coach	Crescent	division	eight
change	coal	cricket	Doctor	either
chant	coast	cricketer	does	elbow
check	coastal	croaked	doesn't	employer
cherries	coat	crook	dog	end
cherry	coax	cross	dole	energy
chews	code	crow	dome	enough
chicken	Col.	cruise	don't	equipment
chief	cold	crumble	done	every
choose	collision	cry	door	everybody
chop	Colonel	crystal	dote	everyone
chops	computer	cubic	doze	everything
choral	conductor	cycle	Dr	everywhere
chore	cone		draw	excite
Christ	confusion		drawer	excursion
christen	consideration		drawn	exhale

Name

Continued from P113

wordbank

exhaust	fit	fought	garlic	guy
exit	fixture	four	gave	gymnasium
explorer	flaw	fox	gent	gymnastics
export	float	foxes	ghastly	gypsy
exposed	floor	Fr	ghost	
express	floppy disk	frantic	ghostly	
extend	flour	fraud	giant	**Hh**
	flower	fraught	gigantic	hack
	foe	freight	gin	half
Ff	followed	Fri.	giraffe	haloes
fall	food	Friday	give	halve
fallen	fool	friend	glow	ham
family	foot	frieze	go	hand
famous	football	fro	goat	handkerchief
fancy	for	frog	good	handkerchiefs
fantastic	fore	frolic	goose	handle
farmer	forearm	froze	governor	happy
farther	forecast	fruit	great	hard
fast	forecourt	fudge	grey	hasn't
Father	forefathers	fund	grief	haste
fault	forefront	fungus	groan	hats
favourite	forego	funny	groaned	haul
fawn	foreground	fur	groom	have
fell	forehand	furniture	grow	hawk
festival	forehead		guard	he'll
field	foreman		guess	heal
fiend	foretell	**Gg**	guest	heel
fine	forewarned	gallows	guide	height
first	foreword	game	guillotine	heliport
fish	forget	garage	guilty	hero
fist	forgot	gardener	guitar	heroes

Continued from P114

word bank

hi-fi	isn't	lasses	master	mode
hippo	it'll	laugh	match	mole
hippopotamus		launch	material	monorail
hippos		law	mathematics	monsoon
hoard	**Jj**	lawn	matter	moon
hoax	jaw	lawyer	mayor	moor
hoe	Jock	learn	maze	more
hold	Joe	lecture	me	motel
hole	joke	lent	meadow	motor
holiday	jostle	lips	meal	mow
honest	juice	list	mean	Mr
honestly	just	lives	meaning	muck
hood		loaf	means	muddle
hook		local	meant	multiply
hope	**Kk**	locate	measles	music
horrific	Keith	location	meat	must
hose	kilo	lone	meddle	mustn't
hour	kilogram	lonely	medical	mystery
huge	kilos	loose	men	
	kind	loud	microchip	
	knew	low	microwave	**Nn**
Ii	knife		middle	narrow
I'll	knight		miner	NATO
ice	knives	**Mm**	minister	naughty
ignore	know	magic	mint	navies
illness		Maj.	missed	neighbour
indecently		Major	mist	neither
information	**Ll**	marsh	Mister	nest
inspection	lap	Mary	mixture	news
instructor	laser	mash	moan	niece
invention	lass	mast	moat	night

			Rr	roar
no	parliament	potato	radar	rock
nobody	particle	pound	raffle	rode
nook	pasta	prawn	rain	roe
noon	pastry	prawns	raise	Roland
nor	pause	prey	RAM	role
note	paw	priest	range	roll
notice	pebble	printer	raw	Roman
nought	pencil	Prof.	rays	Romany
nuclear	people	Professor	Rd	roof
	permission	pronounce	receipt	roost
	persuasion	Prov.	receive	root
Oo	photo	provide	received	rotate
obey	photograph	provision	record	rotation
oboe	photos	Provost	recruit	rough
occupation	piano	puncture	reign	rust
octopus	pianoforte	punt	rein	rustic
Olympic	pianos	python	replied	rustle
one	picnic		reply	
organisation	picture		restore	
ought	piece	**Qq**		
outside	pizza	quadrilateral	Rev.	**Ss**
owl	plough	quadruped	Reverend	salmon
own	poke	quadruplets	reward	sand
	pole	qualify	rhino	satisfy
	pond	quart	rhinoceros	sauce
	poor	quarter	rhinos	saucer
Pp	population	quartet	ridden	sausage
pm	portion	quietly	ride	saw
palm	post-war	quinquireme	right	sawn
panic	postpone	quintet	ring	scene
parade	postscript	quintuplets	Road	school
park				

Continued on P117

Continued from P116

wordbank

scissors	shadow	smog	spit	stoke
scoop	shadows	snow	spite	stood
score	sharp	snuggle	splade	stool
scramble	she'll	so	spoil	store
scratch	sheaf	soap	spoke	stove
scratches	sheaves	soar	spoon	straddle
scratching	sheep	sober	sport	strain
scrawl	Sheila	social	sprang	strange
scream	shelf	society	spray	strangle
screw	shell	socks	spree	strap
scribble	shells	sofa	Spring	straw
scroll	shelves	solar	sprinkle	stray
scuba	ships	sold	sprinkles	stream
sculptor	shirt	sole	sprinkling	Street
sea-shore	shoal	solo	sprint	strength
sealing	shook	something	sprout	stress
see	shoot	son	sprung	stretcher
seen	shore	sonar	square	stride
seize	shouldn't	sore	squid	strike
seldom	show	sow	squirrel	string
send	shriek	spaceship	Sr	stroke
sensation	sincerely	spades	St	strokes
sent	Sister	spaghetti	stadium	stroking
separation	sky	sparkled	station	stroll
Sept.	slant	speak	stay	struggle
September	sleigh	spectacle	stayed	suit
septennial	slices	spectacles	steak	sun
septet	slide	spectator	steal	sunny
serviette	slowly	spell	steel	survey
sextet	sluice	spin	still	survivor
shade	small	spirit	stoat	swarm

Name

Continued from P117 **wordbank**

swim	thyme	tripod	**Ww**	wolf
swollen	tick	troll	wait	wolves
	tiger	troop	war	won
	to	trousers	ward	won't
Tt	toad	tug-o-war	wardrobe	wood
taste	toe	tummy	warm	wool
taught	toes	twins	warning	wore
teacher	told	two	wart	wouldn't
temperature	toll	typhoon	wasn't	woven
terrible	tomato		waste	wrestling
terrified	tomatoes		we'll	wright
terrify	tone	**Uu**	weal	wring
Thames	too	UNESCO	weather	wrist
thaw	took	unicycle	wedding	write
their	topic	uniform	weigh	wrought
there	total	unison	weight	
they	tote	unit	weir	
they'll	tough	united	went	**Yy**
they're	towards		wettest	yellow
thief	towel		wharf	yoghurt
thieves	tragic	**Vv**	wheel	you'll
thing	traitor	veil	where	yours
thistle	traveller	vein	whistle	
Thomas	triangle	video	whole	
thorough	tricolour	village	wife	**Zz**
thoroughly	tricycle	VIP	wind	zone
though	triennial	vote	window	
thought	trifle		windy	
throat	trio		witch	
through	triplets		witches	
throw	triplicate		wives	

Objective: Spell words containing *ie* and *ei*.

'ie' or 'ee'?

Many words that have the **ee** sound are written **ie**.

For example: **brief**

But if a **c** comes before the **ee** sound, it is usually written **ei**.

For example: **receive** (**ei** has the sound **ee** but comes after a **c**)

1. Complete these words using **ie** or **ei**. Check your spelling.

ch_____f   gr_____f   p_____ce   rec_____pt   dec_____ve

f_____ld   n_____ce   pr_____st   bel_____ve   th_____f

2. Here are some words which do not follow the general 'rule'. Say each one then underline the tricky part. Write each word in a sentence.

seize

_____

height

_____

reign

_____

neighbour

_____

Name

Objective: Spell words with the *aw* sound.

Supplementary unit **2** See Units 2 & 9 **pages 30–1 & 46**

Crawler

In many words, **aw** and **au** sound the same; **ar** sometimes sounds like **aw**, too.

For example: **warm**

1. Say these words aloud.

straw	claw	yawn	crawl	August	pause
because	launch	warm	reward	wardrobe	quarter

2. Now use some of the words above to finish these sentences.

The cat drew in its _____s when its owner stroked it.

He _____ed _____ he was so tired.

I like to use a _____ when I drink milk.

Is it _____ to seven yet?

She put her clothes in the _____.

He walked and walked without a single _____.

Objective: Spell words containing
s consonant blends and digraphs.

Supplementary unit **3** See Unit 3 **page 32**

Birthday box

1. Add the word beginnings in the birthday present to the word bases.
Make as many words as you can. The first one has been done for you.

-ake

shake

_____

_____

_____

| sh | sl | sc |
| sp | st | sk |

-ate

_____

_____

_____

_____

-ore

_____

_____

_____

_____

-ale

_____

_____

_____

_____

-ell

_____

_____

_____

_____

-ot

_____

_____

_____

_____

-are

_____

_____

_____

_____

-ip

_____

_____

_____

_____

-ow

_____

_____

_____

_____

-y

_____

_____

_____

_____

Name

Objective: Spell various words in their plural forms.

Supplementary unit 4   See Unit 3 **page 33**

All kinds of plurals

1. There are all kinds of plural words needed in the sentences below. Fill in the plural of each of the words in brackets. Think carefully before you write them in. Some words are the same in the singular *and* the plural.

The (lady) _____ were quite upset because they had not

received any (reply) _____ to their letters.

My friend saw a flock of (sheep) _____ in the field.

In autumn the (leaf) _____ begin to fall from the trees.

Their (baby) _____ were crying all night.

They caught two large (salmon) _____ in Scotland.

Have you put the (box) _____ back on the

(shelf) _____?

Birthday bike

1. Finish these sentences using **'s** contractions.

It_____ going to be fun at the museum. There_____ so much to see.

Bill_____ coming too. He_____ bringing his sister. She_____ only eight.

2. Finish the wheel of your birthday bike by drawing in the spokes. Join the words near the tyre to the **'s** in the hub. Write the new contractions in the spaces down the page.

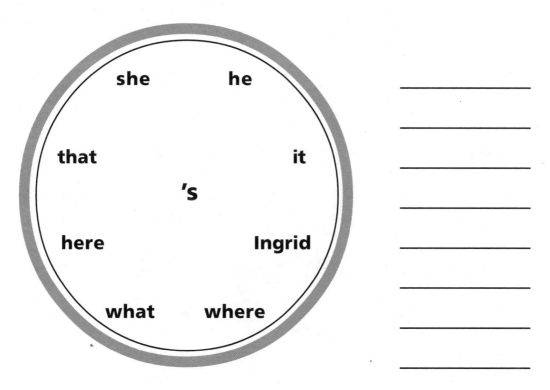

she	he
that	it
's	
here	Ingrid
what	where

_____

_____

_____

_____

_____

_____

_____

_____

3. Write the contractions in the brackets. The first one has been done for you.

"Ingrid is (_Ingrid's_) coming on the train with us. She is (_____)

bringing John. He is (_____) her cousin," I said. "What is

(_____) he like?"

"He is (_____) really nice; he is (_____) a good tennis

player, too," Bill replied. "Where is (_____) the train going?"

Name

Objective: Add the suffixes *ing* and *ed* to verbs with *l* endings.

Supplementary unit **6** See Unit 5 **pages 36–7**

Tunnel travel

When we add **ing** and **ed** to verbs ending in **l**, with consonant–vowel–consonant (CVC), we double the **l**.

For example: sho**vel** – shove**lling** – shove**lled**

Verbs that end in le drop the e before adding ing and ed.

For example: buck**le** – buck**ling** – buck**led**

1. Read these **l** words aloud.

| tremble | bottle | snuggle | signal | total |
| tunnel | struggle | travel | double | |

2. Add **ing** or **d** to the words above before using them to fill the spaces in these sentences.

He _____ when he walked into the dark, cold cave.

We were _____ to Scotland by coach.

All the milk had been _____ .

She was _____ to us to stop the train.

He _____ the number 5; the answer was 10.

They had _____ their way out of the cave.

Supplementary unit **7** See Unit 6 **page 38**

Homophone crossword

1. Complete this crossword. Check against the homophones in the box below to see if you are correct.

Across

2. A long-legged bird.
3. A type of shellfish.
6. You measure this when you get on the scales.
7. You drive a car on this.
9. A cat's feet.

Down

1. A king or queen sits on this.
3. This can make it hard to see on some mornings.
4. You climb these when you go up.
5. A little river.
8. There are seven in a week.

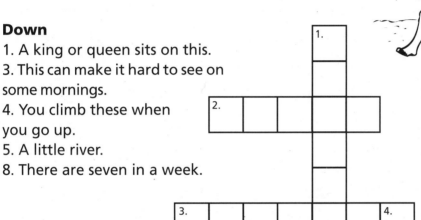

thrown	muscles	creak	rode	throne	missed	
creek	daze	stork	mist	weight	days	stalk
stares	wait	pause	mussels	stairs	road	paws

Name

Supplementary unit **8** See Unit 7 **page 42**

A boat on the beach

In many **oa** words, the second vowel (**a**) is not sounded.
In many **ea** words, the vowel **a** is not sounded.
In many cases, the **o** and **e** are given their long vowel sounds.

For example: **road** and **heat**

1. Say these **oa** and **ea** words aloud, then choose some to use in the sentences below.

coat	sweater	cloak	bread	coach
teapot	meat	toad	beard	moan
groan	thread	loan	feather	spread

The girl dressed herself in her c_____

and s_____.

The man with the long, white b_____

fastened a c_____ round his shoulders.

She was as light as a f_____ so I could carry her easily.

I heard a m_____ from the lady who had been knocked down.

Did I hear you gr_____ when you hurt your leg?

I found it difficult to th_____ the small needle.

TOAD ROAD

Photocopiable ■ SCHOLASTIC

Supplementary unit 9 See Units 8–9 **pages 44–5 & 47**

A bug's life

1. Think about arranging these words in alphabetical order.

> gutter   gale   glide   general   grave

2. Write down the second letter of each word.

_____   _____   _____   _____   _____

3. Now put these second letters in alphabetical order.

_____   _____   _____   _____   _____

4. Arrange the words in alphabetical order, going across.

_____   _____   _____

_____   _____

5. Arrange these words in alphabetical order in your workbook.

> scene   cyclone   area   curve   sap

Quick alphabetical order quiz

	Yes	No
Does **L** come before **F**?		
Does **M** come before **P**?		
Does **fly** come before **bug**?		
Does **Fl** come before **Fr**?		
Does **apple** come before **arc**?		

6. Use your dictionary to find these words. Write down the next word listed in your dictionary in your workbook.

> dew   satellite   graph   pest   aquarium

Name

Objective: Find words in a dictionary.

Supplementary unit **10** See Units 8 &18 **pages 44–5 & 66–7**

Alphabet song

Here's some practice on finding words in a dictionary.

1. In what order would these words come in the dictionary? Write them in the correct order in your workbook.

| zero | present | adore | tree | Christmas |

Handy hint: to find words quickly in your dictionary, keep a mental picture of the alphabet in your head.

First, think of the old alphabet song.

a b c d e f g   h i j k l m n   o p q r s t u   v w x y z

Next, think that **m** and **n** are right in the middle. There are 12 letters on either side of them.

a b c d e f g h i j k l   o p q r s t u v w x y z

Now you simply ask yourself:

Is the word in the first part of the alphabet or the second part?

If it is in the first part, it is in the first part of the dictionary; if in the second, nearer to the end.

2. Practise finding words in your dictionary that start with **b**, **m** or **w**. Find five words for each letter.

My **b** words are: _____

_____

My **m** words are: _____

_____

My **w** words are: _____

_____

Photocopiable **SCHOLASTIC**

Name

Supplementary unit **11** See Unit 9 **page 46**

In a small hall

1. These words all have an **aw** sound. Use them to label the pictures.

stall   bald   tall   ball   stalk   small   hall

_____

_____ man   _____ man

wheat _____   _____ man   tea _____

Notice that in each **aw** word the **a** is followed by two consonants.

For example: ba**ll**   ba**ld**   sta**lk**

2. Write these sentences in your workbook, correcting the spellings.

Can I cal you in the morning?

Don't fal out of the tree.

Al the dodgem cars are full.

Mark the spot with this chork.

Can you still work to the car?

3. Check your spellings using your wordbank.

Name

Paul's ball

1. Complete this crossword, using words that have the **aw** sound.

Across
4. To love very much (a__o__e).
5. A corn st_____.
7. Drag along. Rhymes with Paul (h_____).
9. The second word in racecourse.
10. Rhymes with crawl (sp_____l).

Down
1. I c_____ the train to the showground.
2 I can throw it (b_____).
3. I do it with a pencil (dr_____).
6. Forever (a__w__ys).
8. Lions do it (r_____).

2. Make word families from these bases: **all**, **aw**, **alk**, **awl**, **aught**, **ore**, **oar**. An example of each has been done for you already.

ball	draw	stalk	sprawl

caught	adore	roar

Name

Supplementary unit **13** See Unit 10 **page 48**

Skirts and shirts

 ur and **ir** sound the same. Say **burn** and **shirt** aloud.

1. Write **ur** or **ir** to complete these words. Then say each word aloud.

sk_____t   m_____m_____   th_____sty

b_____d   b_____n   c_____l

f_____m   h_____t   th_____ty

t_____n   g_____l   ch_____ch

2. Read these sentences aloud. Write the correct **ur** and **ir** word in the spaces. Look–Say–Cover–Write–Check!

The g_____ was wearing a red s_____.

The baby had black, c_____y hair.

Are those black_____s in the trees?

I was hot and t_____ after
the long walk.

Did you h_____ yourself
when you fell?

There are t_____ days
in September.

Name

Stop and think

1. Write **e**, **i**, or **y** in the spaces to complete these words. Then say each word and listen to the **c** as **s**.

c___metery   c___ntury   c___rcle

c___ty   c___clone   c___lery

c___rtificate   c___stern   c___cle

spac___   c___ment   c___der

c___trus   c___linder   rec___ive

2. Write the words out here.

_____

_____

_____

_____

_____

3. Read these sentences aloud (pause at full stops and semicolons). Write in the correct **c** word in the spaces. Don't just copy. Use Look–Say–Cover–Write–Check!

She was given a _____ for passing her music exam.

Some children don't like carrots and _____; but I do!

We all stood in a large _____ to play the game.

He rode his _____ to school.

Dead people are buried in the _____.

Did you r_____ my birthday card?

Objective: Use *dis*, *mis* or *un* prefixes.

Supplementary unit 15 See Unit 11 **page 51**

Opposites

1. Write down the meanings of these words.

disappear _____

misunderstood _____

unhappy _____

🔍 The prefix **dis** is from Latin. When we add it to a word, we make the word have the opposite meaning.

2. Write the words that mean the *opposites* of these.

abled _____ charge _____

agree _____ connect _____

🔍 The prefix **mis** comes from the French language. When we add it to a word, we make that word have a negative meaning.

3. Write the words that mean the *opposites* of these.

guided _____ judge _____

behave _____ name _____

fire _____ read _____

🔍 The prefix **un** comes from Old English. When we add it to a word, we make the word have the opposite meaning.

4. Write the words that mean the *opposites* of these.

conscious _____ button _____

known _____ even _____

done _____ seen _____

Objective: Spell *oa, or, ore, oar* and *oor* words.

Supplementary unit **18** See Unit 14 **page 58**

Party time

1. Finish the words in these sentences using **ore**, **or** and **oar**.

There were m_____ than f_____ty people at the party.

The noise was a mighty r_____ and kept the neighbours awake.

The speeches were b_____ing but the food was ad_____able at Auntie Jane's engagement party.

2. Make words with **aw** sounds from these word bases.

h, b → **oard**

_____
_____

ad, bef, ign, rest → **ore**

_____
_____
_____
_____

c, m, s, w → **ore**

_____
_____
_____
_____

r, s → **oar**

_____
_____

d, fl, m, p, b → **oor**

_____
_____
_____
_____
_____

f, n → **or**

_____
_____

br, abr → **oad**

_____
_____

ch, sc, sh, st, b → **ore**

_____
_____
_____
_____
_____

Name

Supplementary unit 19 **See Unit 15 page 60**

Sailing

1. Complete this **st**, **nt** and **nd** crossword.

Across
2. The beach is made of it.
3. The people in it play instruments.
4. The birds build one before they lay eggs.
5. You clench you fingers to make this.
6. Just above your hand.
7. The sails are attached to it.
8. When it blows, the mast bends.

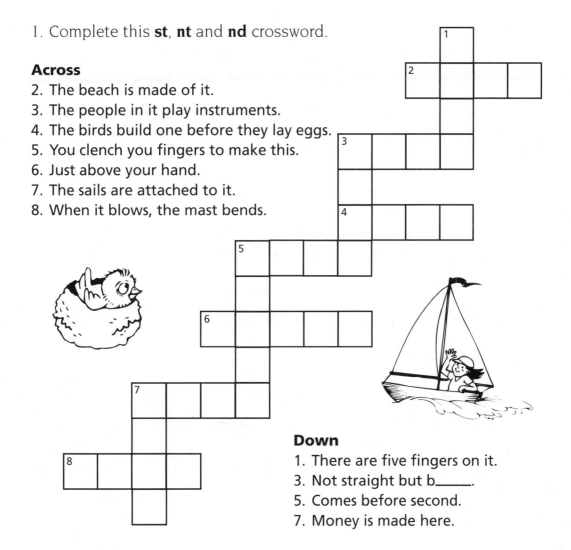

Down
1. There are five fingers on it.
3. Not straight but b_____.
5. Comes before second.
7. Money is made here.

2. Make words from these wheels. Write them in your workbook.

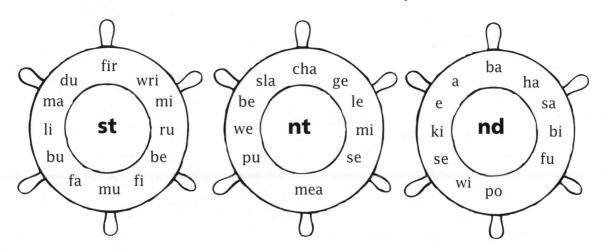

Wheel 1 (st): fir, wri, mi, ru, be, fi, mu, fa, bu, li, ma, du

Wheel 2 (nt): cha, ge, le, mi, se, mea, pu, we, be, sla

Wheel 3 (nd): ba, ha, sa, bi, fu, po, wi, se, ki, e, a

Objective: Spell words ending in *c* or *ck*.

Wedding cake

The **k** sound at the ends of words is spelled with **c** or **ck**. Most words of one syllable end in **ck**. The **k** is only by itself in words like **look** or **hook**.

1. Sort these words into two groups – **c** or **ck**. Write the words onto the correct tier of the wedding cake. .

panic	music	black	garlic	luck	clock	antic
check.	frolic	Jock	frantic	rock	click	

c

ck

2. Make **c** and **ck** words by finishing the steps into the church with **c** or **ck**.

de_____

ha_____

mu_____

du_____

ti_____

cubi_____

Arcti_____

froli_____

Supplementary unit **21** See Unit 16 **page 62**

Silent or sounded

1. Read these words aloud. Some **gh**s have an **f** sound. Others are not sounded at all.

laugh	cough	rough	enough	tough	though	although
thorough	thoroughly	thought	ought	taught	fraught

2. Sort the words into the wedding cake. Write them on the correct tier.

gh with **f** sound

_____ _____ _____

_____ _____ _____

silent **gh**

_____ _____ _____ _____

_____ _____

3. Use some of the **gh** words from above in these sentences. Try to write them from memory – then check. If you spell a word wrongly, correct it, and note *where* you went wrong. Then write the word in your wordbank.

Last night I could not sleep because of a bad c_____. After

three hours I had had e_____ and got up.

The heavy rain made us th_____y wet; I th_____
we would never dry off.

He started to l_____ when his friend told a joke.

A_____ the sea was very r_____, we enjoyed the boat
trip.

You o_____ to clean your teeth after eating all those sweets.

Name _____

One, two, three

1. Do you remember what **uni**, **bi** and **tri** mean?

uni means _____

bi means _____

tri means _____

2. Read these words aloud.

unit	bicycle	tricycle	united
biceps	tripod	unison	bicentennial
triangle	uniform	binoculars	triplets

3. Use **uni**, **bi** or **tri** words to finish these sentences.

The girls wore their school _____s as they rode to school on

their _____s.

The _____ are called, Cathy, Steffie and Marie.

He looked through his _____ so that he could see the
seabirds clearly.

Have you seen the photographer putting his camera on a _____?

The choir sang in _____.

Our club is 200 years old next May; that is our _____ year.

Objective: Spell words with the *o* sound as in *go*, *roll* and *cold*.

Supplementary unit 23 See Unit 19 **pages 70–1**

Let's go for a stroll

1. Make words with the **o** sound as in **go**.

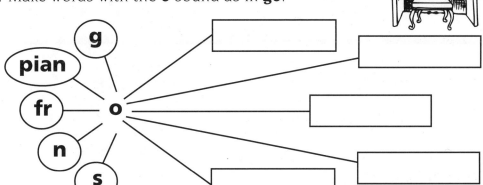

In some words, the **o** as in **roll** sound is found where **o** is followed by two consonants. For example: **cold** and **poll**.

2. Make words with the **o** as in **poll** sound.

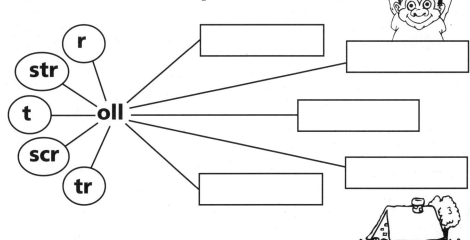

3. Make words with the **o** as in **bold** sound.

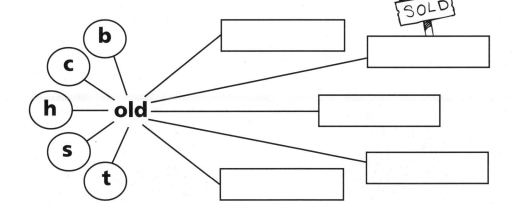

Name

Plurals crossword

1. Fill in the crossword.

Across
1. More than one bat.
2. More than one tomato.
3. More than one sock.
5. More than one lip.
7. More than one hat.
8. More than one navy.
9. More than one toe.

Down
1. More than one buffalo.
4 More than one kilo.
6. More than one piano.
7. More than one halo.

Name

Objective: Spell words beginning with
spr, *scr* and *str* onsets and blends.

Supplementary unit **25** See Unit 20 **page 73**

Wordsearch

1. Ring the **spr**, **scr**, **str** words in this wordsearch. You will find the words across or down. There are 11 words. 4 begin with **str**, 4 begin with **scr**, and 3 begin with **spr**.

s	t	r	a	n	g	e	r
p	q	r	s	t	r	a	p
r	u	s	c	r	e	e	n
u	v	w	r	s	x	y	z
n	a	b	a	c	c	d	e
g	f	s	p	r	a	n	g
s	f	t	e	i	g	h	s
p	i	r	j	b	k	l	c
r	m	e	r	b	o	p	r
e	q	e	r	l	s	t	u
e	s	t	r	e	s	s	b

2. Write the 11 words in your workbook.

3. Choose from the following **spr**, **scr** and **str** words to fill the spaces in the sentences below.

> strangle   straw   strain   sprang   stretcher

In the tug-o-war we were told to take the _____.

They carried William off on a _____.

He put fresh _____ in his horse's stable.

Jamila s_____ ahead at the start.

You cannot use a _____ hold in wrestling.

Name

Objective: Know and spell plurals of words that end in *f* or *fe*.

Supplementary unit **26** See Unit 21 **page 75**

King Henry's crossword

Remember: To make the plural of words ending in **f**, change the **f** to **v** and add **es**. If the word ends in **fe**, change the **f** to **v** and add **s**.

For example: cal**f** – cal**ves**   kni**fe** – kni**ves**

1. Complete this crossword.

Across

3. You put books on these.
4. More than one sheaf.
6. A cat has nine _____.
7. King Henry VIII had six _____.

Down

1. More than one wolf.
2. The _____ fell from the tree in autumn.
5. I was robbed by four _____.

Objectives: Spell and use abbreviations in context. Use formal letter-writing conventions.

Thank-you note

1. Write these in their abbreviated forms.

Colonel Bogey _____

Major Brown _____

Bardwell Crescent _____

September _____

Friday _____

2. Write a short note to Doctor Fielding, thanking him for presenting the prizes at the swimming carnival.
His address is 12 Riverview Drive, Southwell, Lancashire, SR9 0TT.
Use shortened forms where possible.

> Your address and today's date

Dear _____ ,

_____

_____

_____

_____

_____

_____

Yours sincerely,

_____

> Name of doctor

> Doctor Fielding's address

> Your name

Objective: Find words on a dictionary page.

Supplementary unit **28** See Unit 23 **pages 78–9**

Guide words

1. The guide words on a dictionary page are **mask – meant**. Put these words in alphabetical order.

match	1. _____
mean	2. _____
material	3. _____
maze	4. _____
mayor	5. _____
meal	6. _____
master	7. _____
meant	8. _____
meaning	9. _____
meadow	10. _____

2. Will these words appear as word entries on the page?
Tick **yes** or **no** for each word.

Word	Yes	No
mash		
medical		
mathematics		
matter		
Mary		
means		
marsh		
meat		

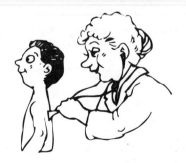

Name _____   **Objective:** Use *magic e* with *a, i* and *o.*

Magic e

 Remember that **magic e** may make vowels sound like their name.
For example: **cage**, **tide** and **code**.

1. Make as many words as you can with the long **a** sound.

```
   (c)
          _____   _____   _____
   (s)
       age _____   _____   _____
       ake
   (t) ame _____   _____
   (st)
          _____   _____
```

2. Make as many words as you can with the long **i** sound.

```
   (t)
          _____   _____
   (m)
       ide _____   _____
   (pr) ime _____   _____
   (sl)
          _____
```

3. Make as many words as you can with the long **o** sound.

```
   (ph)(t)
          _____   _____
   (l)
       one _____   _____
       ole
   (st) _____   _____
   (h)(p)
          _____   _____
```

4. Write one sentence using **a** words you have made, one with **i** words
and one with **o** words.

More words like 'guide'

1. Make these **gu** words. For each word, the **u** is silent and the next vowel is sounded instead. Don't forget that **y** may act like a vowel. Say the words aloud.

2. Write the words.

gu   ide   _____

       ess   _____

       y   _____

       itar   _____

       est   _____

       ard   _____

       ilty   _____

       illotine   _____

3. Use some of the **gu** words you have made to complete these sentences.

We went on a cruise to America and had a very good g_____ to show us around.

I need a new string for my g_____.

The children were asking for pennies for the _____.

He felt _____ because he had drunk his brother's tea.

He _____ed that they would be late for the egg and spoon race.

The _____ signalled that the train was ready to leave the station.

Name _____

(**Supplementary unit** **31**) See Unit 25 **page 84**

Weigh that strange steak!

1. Make some long **a** sound word families.

w
fr
eigh-t

_____

_____

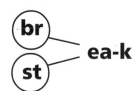

br
st
ea-k

_____

_____

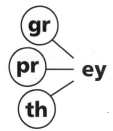

gr
pr
th
ey

_____

_____

_____

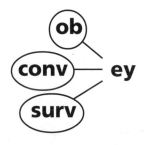

ob
conv
surv
ey

_____

_____

_____

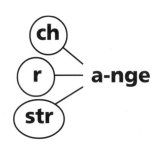

ch
r
str
a-nge

_____

_____

_____

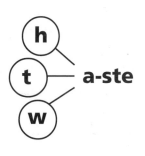

h
t
w
a-ste

_____

_____

_____

Sometimes the long **a** sound is spelled with just **ei** or **eig**.

For example: **vein**   **rein**   **veil**   **reign**

2. Write the correct words in the gaps in these sentences. Pick from the four special words above.

We have lots of _____ s and arteries in our bodies.

I held the _____ s so the horse would not gallop.

The bride had a _____ over her face.

The queen _____ s over her subjects.

Name

What have you bought?

1. Write out the **ought** words from this poem in your workbook.

Very expensive

My mum bought me new school clothes,
They cost a lot I thought.
My mum said they would cost much less
Without the final nought!

Gordon Winch

2. Proof-read this little story. Cross out the words that are spelled wrongly. Write the correct words in the spaces that follow them.

Jack cort _____ a fish when we went on our camping

excursion. His father had taut _____ him how do it. The fish

fort _____ hard but Jack brort _____ it into the shore.

   "Well done, Jack" our teacher said. "You ort _____ to be a
fisherman when you grow up."

3. Fill in the gaps with **aught** or **ought** to finish the words.

d_____er   b_____   th_____t

c_____t   br_____t   wr_____t

t_____t   f_____t

n_____ty   n_____t

sl_____ter   _____t

4. Complete these sentences.

Another word for mischievous: n_____.

A boy and a girl in a family are a son and d_____.

Objectives: Spell words with the prefix *ex*. Spell *sion* words.

Supplementary unit **33** See Unit 26 **pages 86–7**

Journeys

1. Make these **ex** words.

ex hale _____

press _____

it _____

tend _____

cursion _____

port _____

2. Make these **sion** words.

colli **sion** _____

permis _____

confu _____

persua _____

divi _____

provi _____

3. Use some of the words you have made to complete these sentences.

Mum gave her p_____. I _____d a sigh of relief.

Bread, cheese and ham were our p_____s for the

e_____.

There was a terrible c_____ near the motorway e_____.

We hope to e_____ our holiday for another week.

The e_____ train was late; this caused great c_____.

Name _____

(Supplementary unit **34**) See Unit 27 **pages 88–9**

Before and after

Q **Auto** means 'self'. **Anti** means 'against'. **Ante** means 'before'. **Post** means 'after'.

1. Use these prefixes and the word parts in the box to answer the clues.

free from germs _____

destroy bacteria _____

works by itself _____

message at the end of a letter _____

to sign your own name _____

a waiting room _____

before birth _____

to delay _____

natal

septic

matic

graph

pone

script

room

biotics

2. Use the words you have made to complete these sentences. Be careful! Read the *whole* of each sentence first.

At the end of the letter was a p_____ inviting me to his birthday party.

My grandmother did not have an a_____ washing machine.

When I fell ill, the a_____s made me better.

She asked me to wait in an a_____.

She asked the footballer to sign his name in her a_____ book.

Mum put a_____ cream on my sore hand.

It rained so hard they had to p_____ the game.

Before my sister was born, Mum went to a_____ classes.

Photocopiable ■ SCHOLASTIC

Objective: Identify and spell more homophones.

Supplementary unit **35** See Unit 28 **page 90**

At the reef

1. Fill in the spaces by choosing the homophone that makes sense.

The _____(1) was a beautiful colour. To see it you must go

_____(2) out to the edge of the reef. I have not _____(3) anything

_____(4). The fish are brightly-striped. _____(5) _____(6) quick

to catch. If you swim down near the floating _____(7) which marks

the pontoon, you can see thousands of them. Have you ever _____(8)
to the reef?

| **1** choral/coral | **2** father/farther | **3** seen/scene | **4** moor/more |
| **5** They're/Their | **6** to/too | **7** buoy/boy | **8** bean/been |

2. Fill in this homophone crossword.

Across
1. Found on a tree (bow/bough).
2. Opposite to floor (sealing/ceiling).
4. A strange noise (creek/creak).
6. After **day** (knight/night).
7. Is pretty and grows on a plant
(flower/flour).

Down
1. Put on a horse (bridal/bridle).
3. How heavy you are (wait/weight).
4. To pick (chews/choose).
5. To take something not your own
(steal/steel).

Objective: Make and understand compound words and portmanteaux.

Patchwords

 Some words we use are made by putting together other words or parts of words.

For example: **lunch** and **breakfast** make **brunch**
smoke and **fog** make **smog**

1. Work out which words make these words.

_____ and _____ make **motel**.

_____ and _____ make **cheeseburger**.

_____ and _____ make **football**.

_____ and _____ make **camcorder**.

 Some words are made to fill a need, such as when something new is invented or discovered.

2. In your workbook, write these new words in sentences, saying what you think they mean. (Note: not *all* of these words are blends of other words.) Check your guesses in a dictionary.

monorail	nuclear	hi-fi	computer	floppy disk
microwave	microchip	cosmonaut	heliport	disco

Name

Supplementary unit **37** See Unit 30 **page 94–5**

Many meanings

1. Some words have more than one meaning. You need to be careful to understand the correct one. Often, they can be verbs or nouns. Use a dictionary to find the multiple meanings of these words.

lap

1. _____

2. _____

3. _____

notice

1. _____

2. _____

record

1. _____

2. _____

3. _____

2. Write the words which have these meanings.

1. a claw
2. a kind of small spike or stud   _____
3. the horny end part of a finger

1. flat or smooth
2. a level piece of country   _____
3. undecorated or simple

1. able to do something
2. a tin container   _____

Name

x**Objective:** Spell words with long and short *oo* sounds.

y

Supplementary unit **38** See Units 31–2 **pages 98 & 100**

Boom! Boom!

1. Make four words for each of these word families.

oom	oot	ool	oo
_____	_____	_____	*bamboo*
_____	_____	_____	_____
_____	_____	_____	_____
_____	_____	_____	_____

2. Write down all the **oo** words you can make from this square.

s	m	t
n	**oo**	d
n	t	h

_____ _____ _____

_____ _____ _____

_____   _____

3. Find 14 **oo** words in this wordsearch. They go across from left to right and straight down from top to bottom.

c	u	c	k	o	o
o	g	l	o	o	m
o	n	p	t	q	o
t	a	t	t	o	o
s	n	o	o	z	e
p	o	o	l	o	v
r	s	t	o	o	p
g	r	o	o	m	w

_____ _____

_____ _____

_____ _____

_____ _____

_____ _____

_____ _____

_____ _____

Objective: Spell and use adjectives ending in *y* with an *i* sound.

Supplementary unit **39** See Unit 31 **page 99**

Happy or grumpy?

Words which describe nouns are **adjectives**. Many adjectives end in **y**.

For example: **hungry**

Notice the **i** sound of the **y**.

1. Use the **y** adjectives in the box to complete the sentences underneath.

busy	grumpy
happy	frosty
rainy	rusty
muddy	

They were too _____ to talk to me.

The winter morning was cold and _____.

Ducks love _____ days.

The _____ nail would not go into the wood.

He was so _____ that he sang while he was baking.

Dad must be in a bad mood because he's so

_____.

Ami and Blackie got all _____ playing in the park.

Name

Push and pull

1. Say these words. Listen to the sound made by the **u**.

bull	push	full	puss
pull	bush	helpful	cushion

2. Using Look–Say–Cover–Write–Check, complete the words in the spaces below.

b _____

f _____

p _____

h _____

p _____

p _____

b _____

c _____

3. Write a sentence for each of these words.

butcher _____

_____

bullet _____

_____

sugar _____

_____

Objective: Recognise and spell words with silent *h*.

Supplementary unit **41** See Unit 32 **page 101**

Ghoulish goings-on

1. Read these silent **h** words.

ghost	honestly	whistle	ghastly
hour	Thames	thyme	

2. Read these sentences, putting in the correct silent **h** words from above. Check in your wordbank that each word is spelled correctly.

I head a noise. At first I thought it was a

g_____, but it was

only the wind.

He felt terrified; his face had turned a

g_____y colour.

I did not take your book;

_____ly, I am telling the truth.

The River T_____ flows through London.

In March we put our watches and clocks forward by one _____.

Cooks often use the herb t_____ when they make stuffing.

The umpire w_____d the end of the match.

Supplementary unit **42** See Unit 34 **page 104**

Is it 'ic' or 'ick'?

> Words ending in **ic** usually have more than one syllable.
> Words ending in **ick** usually have one syllable.

1. Make these **ic** words.

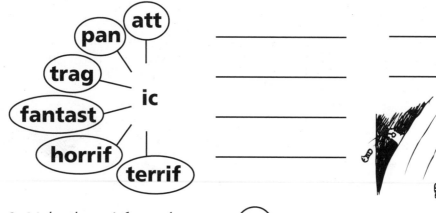

pan · att

trag

fantast · ic

horrif

terrif

_____ _____

_____ _____

_____

_____

2. Make these **ick** words.

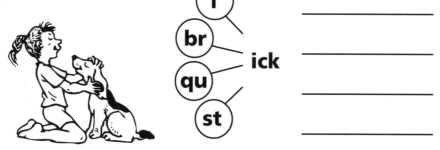

l

br

qu · ick

st

_____

_____

_____

_____

3. Complete each of these sentences using an **ic** or **ick** word that makes sense.

The old house had an a_____ at the very top.

He was in a p_____ when his dog ran away.

The builder built the house from red b_____s.

Mum said I had to be qu_____ or else I would be late for school.

I hate having to l_____ stamps before putting them on letters.

Last night I awoke suddenly from a h_____ dream.

My friends and I had a t_____ time at the pantomime.